BLACKIE·CHAMBERS

MATHEMATICS IN ACTION

Mathematics in Action Group

D1743016

Projects, Problems and Investigations

Blackie and Son Limited
Bishopbriggs
Glasgow G64 2NZ

W & R Chambers Limited
43–45 Annandale Street
Edinburgh EH7 4AZ

7 Leicester Place
London WC2H 7BP

© **Mathematics in Action Group 1990**

Illustrated by *Dickson Huggins Associates and John Martin*
Cover photograph: Courtesy of Rutherford Appleton Laboratory, Oxfordshire

British Library Cataloguing in Publication Data

Mathematics in Action
   Projects, problems and investigations
   1. Mathematics
   I. Mathematics in Action Group
   510

   ISBN 0–216–92946–6
   ISBN 0–550–75746–5 (Chambers)

Printed in Great Britain by Scotprint Ltd, Musselburgh, Scotland

Robin D. Howat, Mathematics Adviser, Ayrshire
Edward C. K. Mullan, Galashiels Academy
Ken Nisbet, Madras College, St Andrews, Fife
Doug Brown, St Anne's High School, Heaton Chapel, Stockport, Cheshire

with
J. L. Hodge, A. G. Robertson

This collection of Projects, Problems and Investigations is taken from Books 5A and 5B of the series of textbooks *Mathematics in Action*.

MiAG June 1990

1 Long-term projects

Over a period of several weeks or months collect and analyse data on one of the following, and write a report about it. **Use as much suitable mathematics as you can.**

a The local weather—temperature, rainfall, wind speed and direction, sunshine and any other factors.

b Your own money—income, saving and spending.

c The absences of pupils in your form, year or school.

d A traffic survey near your home.

e Furnishing and decorating your bedroom.

f The Stocks and Shares 'game'—see page 29.

2 Short-term projects

Choose one or two, and develop them as far as you can.

a Analyse the demand and supply of children's clothes, including the range of sizes and samples of pupils' sizes; availability of large/small sizes; VAT; prices; School Uniforms.

b Analyse a newspaper round. Record the number of each newspaper delivered. Calculate the average pay and time for each paper delivered. How much do people pay for their papers and their delivery? Compare different newsagents. Describe the route.

c Design a tray or container to hold 30 rulers, protractors, compasses and pencils so that a teacher could easily carry a set from room to room. Think about ease of access, counting, carrying, and so on. Make detailed drawings, showing all measurements.
You might be able to make your container in C.D.T.

d Design some items for a children's playground—swings, slides, roundabouts, climbing towers and the like. Make drawings and construct models of some of them. List the materials that would be needed; estimate costs and predict safety factors to be considered.

e Investigate the way in which items are packaged in boxes, tins and different kinds of containers. Open out the containers where possible to find the shape of the material, its area and the volume of the container. Find out how the containers are grouped for transit, how they are stored, the materials used, and so on.

f Investigate the use of water in the house—the volumes of the storage tanks, and the amount of water used daily. Relate the amount to the annual water rate for the house. Calculate the cost of a hot bath versus a shower, central heating and any other services you can think of.

g Make a detailed scale-drawing of a dartboard, describing all the angles and arc lengths. Which areas are aimed at for high/low scores? Design your own board and placing of the numbers.
Make up a new darts game—possibly simulating a sport.

h How fast do you read? How fast do you speak? How long does it take to read a short story compared to listening to a taped copy of it? How much tape would be necessary?
How long would it take to read right through some newspapers?

i Investigate cinema-going—the number and location of cinemas within reach, the number of seats and their prices, lengths of films and popularity of different types; which nights are most popular; effect of television and so on. A questionnaire could be compiled in order to gather some statistics.

j Carry out a survey of the routes pupils take to and from school. Draw a large map of the surrounding area. Use different sized arrows to indicate the number of pupils using the roads. Include a bus survey, and possibly details of the methods of transport used by all the pupils.

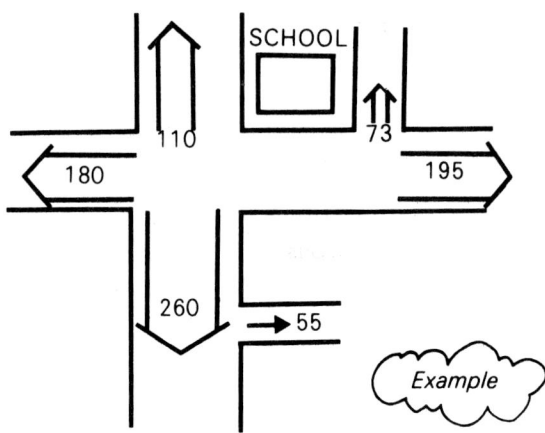

Example

k Use another questionnaire to help you to investigate and analyse pupils' collections of records, discs, radio and video cassettes. Compare the popularity of each type, its cost, its advantages and disadvantages, and the amount of time devoted to it.

l Design a swimming pool, and make a scale model of it.
How much water would the pool need? Area and cost of tiling? How many people could it hold? Investigate the method of heating the water.

m Design a bridge with arches in the shape of parabolas or semicircles. Make a scale model of the bridge.

n Plan a route on the moors or mountains for a 2/3 day hike.
Give details of distances, bearings, gradients, heights, times, camp sites, emergency routes, landmarks and map references.
List items, including food, that you might take with you, and their cost.

o Plan a new garden. Decide on the shape and size, and where you will have paths, lawns, flowers, vegetables, fruit trees, and so on. Make sketches showing the kinds of flowers and vegetables you would grow, their distance apart and cost.
Try to plan a year's work in the garden, with purchases and savings in cost over shop prices.

p Use dice, spinners, home-made cards to devise and simulate a new game. For example, extend this tennis simulation to a full court:

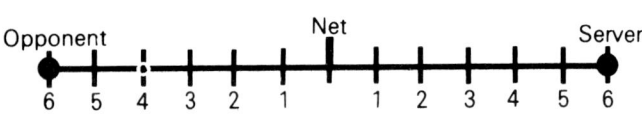

The server is on a '6 spot' then throws 2 dice, and adds the scores together. Failing to clear the net the server can take another turn. By failing again, the opponent serves from his or her own '6 spot'. Thereafter players take turn about, playing from where the ball lands, choosing 1 or 2 dice depending on how close they are to the net.
Points are scored as in tennis. The service is lost by failing to clear the net, or overshooting the other '6 spot'; and so on.

3 Testing and recording projects

a Design a brake-test for a bicycle. Use it to test several bicycles, and produce a Report on the effectiveness of the brakes.

Things to think about—separate tests for front and rear brakes; weight of rider; road surface; wet/dry conditions; stopping distances at different speeds; and safety advice.

b Design an eyesight test based on mathematical ways of measuring and recording results. Use the test on a group of volunteers, and produce a Report on your findings. Things to think about—seeing with one/both eyes; short/long sight; with/without spectacles; colour blindness; field of vision.

c Calculate the distance, time and speed of a train travelling on a model railway, or a car on a model race track. Try to compare these with 'the real thing' by scaling up.

Tiling patterns

Take your choice! Copy and extend some of these patterns of tiles. You will need square or triangular grids to draw them on.

1

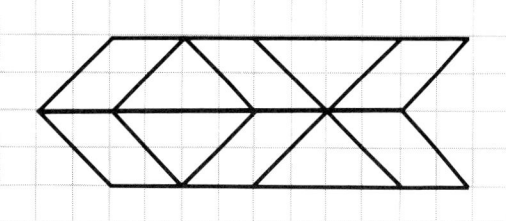

Trapeziums *Hexagons* *Parallelograms and Triangles (or squares)*

2

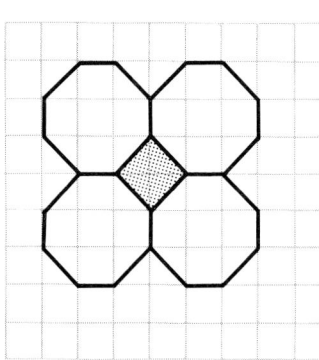
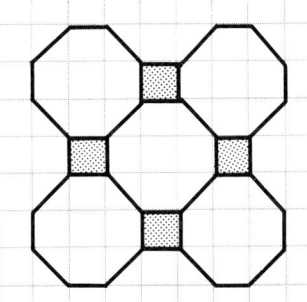
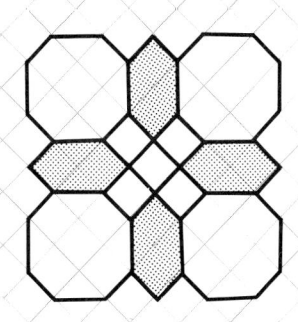

Octagons and squares *Three tiles*

3

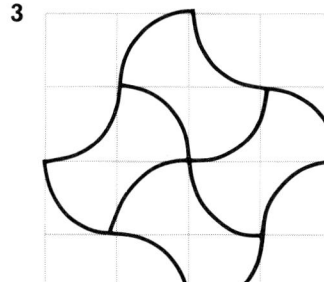
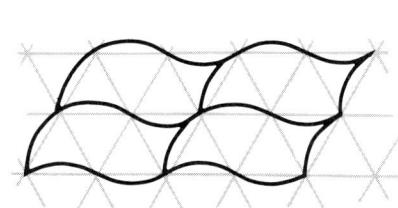
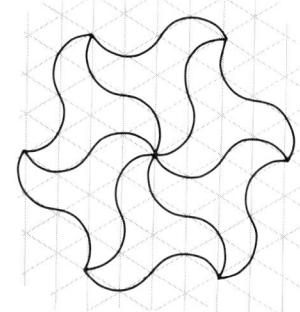

Arcs of circles

4

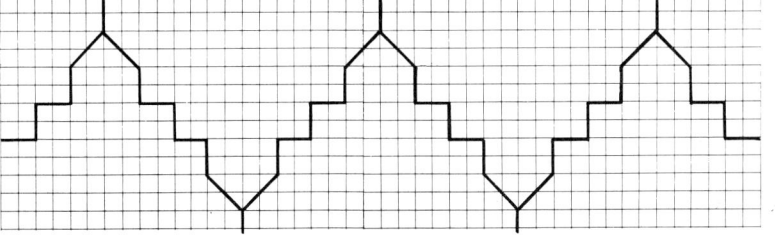
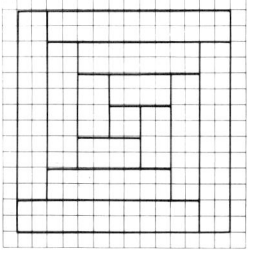

A border tile *Expanding rectangles*

5 Make your own tiling patterns. Describe the shapes in them, and any interesting features. Colour adds to the effect.

Russian multiplication

This is a surprising way to multiply numbers. No calculators needed!

Example Calculate 6×13.

(6×13) Divide the first number by 2 (ignore any remainder), and multiply the second by 2.

3×26 Divide the first number by 2 (ignore any remainder); and multiply the second by 2.

1×52

Rules (i) Score out the products where the *left-hand* number is even.

(ii) Add the remaining numbers on the *right*: $26 + 52 = 78$. Then $6 \times 13 = 78$.

Another example Calculate 74×26.

(74×26) Here $52 + 208 + 1664 = 1924$.

37×52 $74 \times 26 = 1924$. (Check this!)

(18×104)

9×208

(4×416)

(2×832)

1×1664

1 Try these products **a** 8×9 **b** 12×15 **c** 7×25 **d** 51×11

2 Make up some examples of your own. Check the answers.

3 Draw a flowchart for the instructions.

Hidden words

All the words below, about a circle, are hidden in this rectangle of letters. They may be horizontal, vertical or diagonal, in either direction.

E	C	N	E	R	E	F	M	U	C	R	I	C
S	S	A	R	C	O	N	D	R	A	A	T	R
S	E	C	T	O	R	R	T	E	O	D	A	A
O	G	C	N	E	O	A	R	T	S	I	N	T
M	M	D	E	H	G	A	H	E	G	U	G	E
G	E	L	C	R	I	C	I	M	E	S	C	O
R	N	M	A	T	H	S	P	A	R	T	E	N
A	T	A	N	G	E	N	T	I	I	I	N	T
D	A	C	T	I	O	N	A	D	D	R	O	C

a Copy the grid, and pencil a line around these words:

ARC	CHORD	RADIUS	SEGMENT
AREA	CIRCUMFERENCE	PI	SEMICIRCLE
CENTRE	DIAMETER	SECTOR	TANGENT

b Using a diagram, or otherwise, describe each word.

c Can you find a short version of this book's title hidden in the letters (not necessarily in the same line)?

Crossword puzzles

Make a collection of crosswords from newspapers and magazines.

a Calculate the number of:

(i) squares (ii) black squares (iii) white squares

(iv) white squares as a percentage of the total number of squares (v) clues.

b Investigate: (i) lines of symmetry   (ii) rotational symmetry, in the pattern of black squares.
c Use symmetry to design a crossword-type grid of your own.

Addition table squares

+	1	2	3	4	5	6	7	8	9
1	2	3	4	5	6	7	8	9	10
2	3	4	5	6	7	8	9	10	11
3	4	5	6	7	8	9	10	11	12
4	5	6	7	8	9	10	11	12	13
5	6	7	8	9	10	11	12	13	14
6	7	8	9	10	11	12	13	14	15
7	8	9	10	11	12	13	14	15	16
8	9	10	11	12	13	14	15	16	17
9	10	11	12	13	14	15	16	17	18

Belle studies an addition table.
She draws a square round four numbers.

1 a

9	10
10	11

She *adds* diagonally opposite numbers.
What does she find?
Try more squares in other parts of the table.

b

x	?
?	?

x is the top left-hand number in a square.
Draw a square, with *x* in it, and fill in the other three terms.
Add diagonally opposite terms. What do you find?

2 a

9	10
10	11

This time Belle *multiplies* diagonals.
What does she find?

Try more squares in other parts of the table. Can you find a rule?

b Use the terms you wrote down in **1 b** to *prove* your rule.

3 Which line of numbers in the table is a line of symmetry for all the numbers?

Painted faces

1 layer

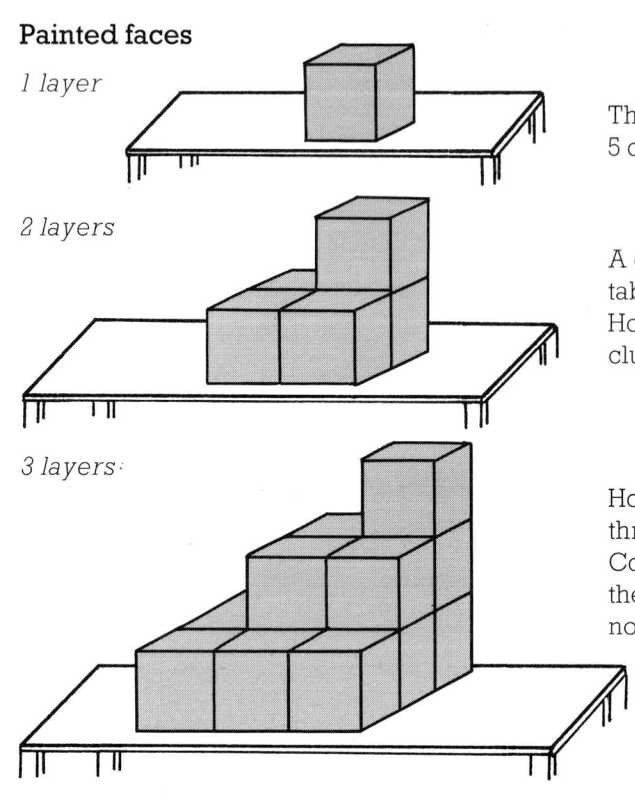

This cube is sitting on a table.
5 of its faces can be painted.

2 layers

A cube is placed on top of four others on the table.
How many faces can be painted now (including those on the top cube)?

3 layers

How many faces can be painted on these three layers of cubes?
Copy the diagram and add a fourth layer at the bottom. How many faces can be painted now?

Number of layers	1	2	3	4	5	6		n
Number of painted faces	5 1×5	$5 + \ldots$ $= \ldots$ $2 \times \ldots$	$3 \times \ldots$					

Copy and complete this table. By finding the pattern you should be able to fill in the number of painted faces for n layers of cubes.

Gift cards

Mr and Mrs Locket run a gift shop.
They decide to sell gift cards worth £1, £2, £3 . . . up to £12. The value is made up of gift stamps stuck on the cards.

They agree to have:
(i) only 3 different stamp values   (ii) not more than 3 stamps on a card.
Fiona, Eve and Colin offer to choose 3 stamps, and calculate the values of the gift cards using their stamps.

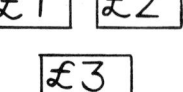

Fiona's choice

Eve's choice

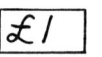

Colin's choice

a Copy and complete the table up to a total value of £12.

Total value	Fiona			Eve			Colin		
	£1	£2	£3	£1	£2	£5	£1	£3	£6
£1	✓			✓			✓		
£2		✓			✓		✓✓		
£3			✓	✓	✓			✓	

b What is the greatest value (going up in steps of £1) that each set of stamps can make?
c Whose choice of stamps was best? Whose was not very good?
d Can you find a better choice of 3 stamps?

Armchair puzzles

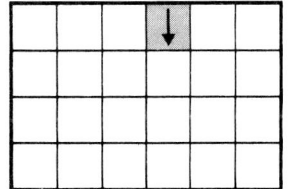 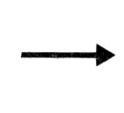 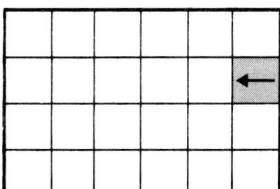

Starting position of armchair in room.

The armchair has to be moved to this position in the room. How was it done? Read on.

How to move an armchair: Choose one of the four legs. Turn it about that leg through $\frac{1}{4}$, $\frac{1}{2}$ or $\frac{3}{4}$ of a complete turn (clockwise or anticlockwise). Repeat as necessary.

Solution: $\frac{1}{4}$ turn anticlockwise, then $\frac{1}{2}$ turn anticlockwise. See below (use a small card square with an arrow on it, on squared paper, if you wish):

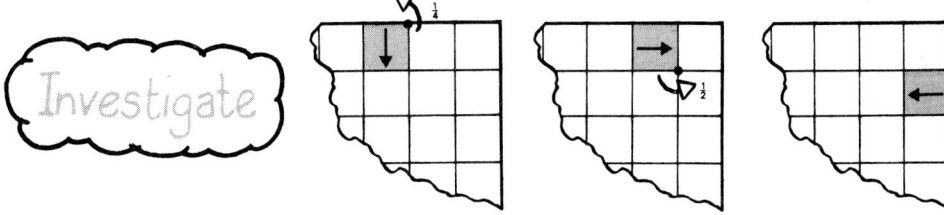

1 With the same starting position as before, investigate which final positions are possible around the edges of the room.
The armchair must always face in towards the centre of the room.

2 Try changing the starting position, or the size of the room, or the shape of the furniture.

Bus route numbers

Newtown's buses display a 2 digit number to show their route to passengers.

Investigate the number of routes that can be displayed with:

1 *Two 'windows'*

a

Each window shows a number from 0 to 9. Numbers can be repeated, for example 44.

b (i)

The first window shows a number from 0 to 9, the second a letter from A to Z.

(ii) One 'window' shows a number, the other a letter, for example A6, or 6A.

2 *Three 'windows'*

Investigate the number of routes that can be shown using:

a numbers only **b** letters only.

c mixtures of numbers and letters.

(Make your own rules for where letters and numbers may go.)

Investigate the British (and other?) systems of vehicle registration numbers over the years.

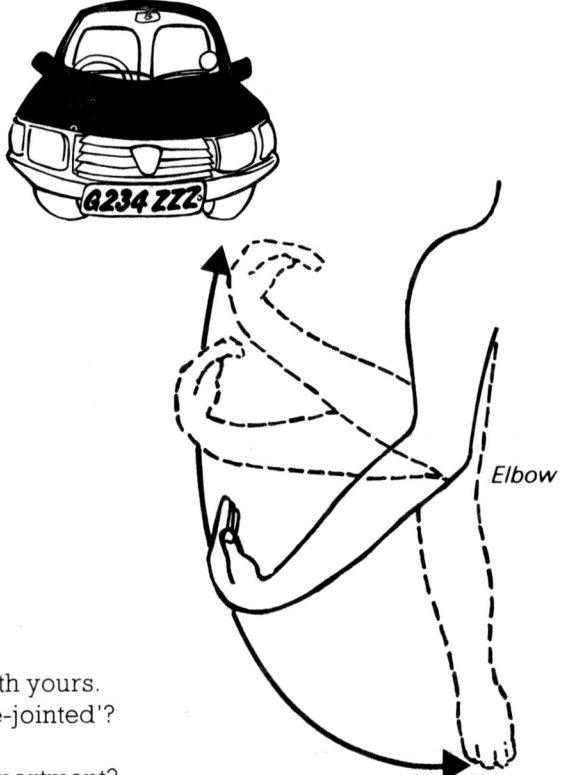

The geometry of your bones and joints

1 Your body is full of joints which allow your fingers, wrists, arms, legs,..., to turn through all kinds of angles. Make a table, and fill in approximate angles of rotation:

Part of body	Joint	Angle (degrees)
Hand	Wrist	
Thumb	Knuckle	

Elbow

2 Ask some friends to compare their angles with yours. Are there any differences? Is anyone 'double-jointed'?

3 Is there a human skeleton in your Biology Department? If so, study some of its joints. Each one allows a different movement for a certain reason. Describe some of the joints, the movements and the angles.

Swimming 100 metres, using different strokes

1 *World record times, 1987*

Stroke	Backstroke	Breaststroke	Butterfly	Freestyle
Men	55·17 s	1 min 1·65 s	52·84 s	48·74 s
Women	1 min 0·59 s	1 min 7·91 s	57·93 s	54·73 s

    a Copy the table, writing the times to the nearest second.
    b Calculate the average speed, to the nearest 0·1 m/s, for each stroke for:
      (i) men   (ii) women.
    c List the strokes in order of speed.
    d For which stroke is the women's time: (i) closest to   (ii) furthest from, the men's time?

2 *World record times for men's freestyle, 1987*

Distance	50 m	100 m	200 m	400 m
Time	22·32 s	48·74 s	1 min 47·44 s	3 min 47·80 s

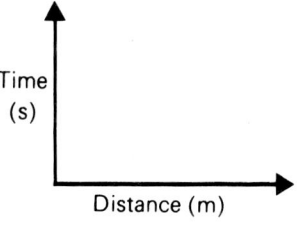

    a Copy the table, writing the times to the nearest second.
    b Draw a graph of distance against time.
    c Calculate the average speed, to the nearest 0·1 m/s, for each distance.
    d Write a sentence about the way in which the speed changes for different distances.

3 Record your own or a friend's times for different strokes and distances. How do they compare with the world records?

Design symmetry

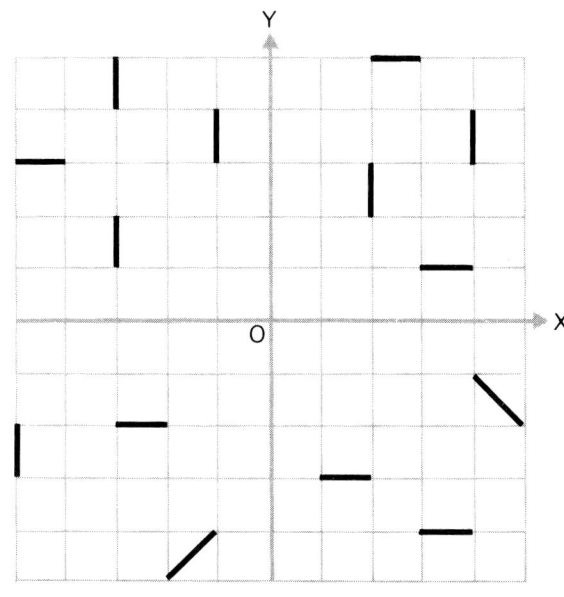

1 a Choose one of the black lines.
    Reflect it in the *x*-axis, then in the *y*-axis, then in the *x*-axis, and so on, until you are back to the start.
  b Do this for every black line until you have four polygons.

2 Design your own shape on a squared grid, and break it up into different parts. It could be a geometric shape, or an animal, or … Ask a friend to try to put it together again as in question **1**.

A day trip

The pupils in Mrs Ndabe's form class, 4C, are planning a day trip. There are five suggestions for the outing, and the pupils list their preference in order, 1–5.

Pupil	Seaside	London	Zoo	Concert	Funfair
J.A.	1	4	2	5	3
W.A.	5	1	3	4	2
R.B.	1	2	5	3	4
T.C.	3	5	2	1	4
S.E.	5	1	3	4	2
J.F.	1	5	2	3	4
T.F.	5	4	2	1	3
I.H.	2	1	5	3	4
J.M.	1	2	5	4	3
P.M.	4	1	5	3	2
R.M.	1	4	2	5	3
S.N.	5	2	3	1	4
A.P.	5	1	4	3	2
J.R.	4	2	5	1	3
T.R.	1	5	2	3	4
W.R.	5	1	3	4	2
K.S.	1	5	2	4	3
N.S.	4	2	5	1	3
C.T.	5	1	3	4	2
G.T.	1	2	5	3	4
S.T.	1	5	2	3	4
A.W.	5	4	2	1	3
K.W.	5	4	2	1	3
P.Y.	1	5	2	3	4
R.Y.	1	5	2	4	3
T.Y.	5	2	3	1	4

1 Four friends had exactly the same preference. What are their initials?

2 a Make a tally chart for each suggestion, like this one.

Preference	Tally	Frequency
1	ⅢⅠ ⅢⅠ Ⅰ	11
2		
3		
4		
5		

b Which destination has most:
(i) first choices   (ii) last choices?

3 Try to use your statistics to make an argument for going to each place.

4 Sheila Tyson suggests giving points to each destination:
5 points for each 1st choice, 4 points for 2nd, 3 points for 3rd, 2 points for 4th and 1 point for 5th. Which destination would be chosen using this system?

5 Mrs Ndabe has to decide on the destination.
Where do you think they ought to go? Explain how you reach a decision.

6 In the end she decided that the form could split up and go to two different places:
a Is it possible for all the pupils to have:
(i) their first choice   (ii) their first or second choice?
b Which two places did she choose? List the initials of the pupils going to each one.

7 Carry out a similar task for an outing for your class.
Choose possible destinations, arrange a survey, and take into account any other factors involved.

Equal shares

Farmer Giles gives his two daughters one of his rectangular fields, which can be marked off in square sections as shown.

They have to share the field by taking an equal number of square sections each.

The daughters decide to investigate all the ways in which this can be done.

2 by 1 field

Only 1 way, as ... is just the same.

2 by 2 field

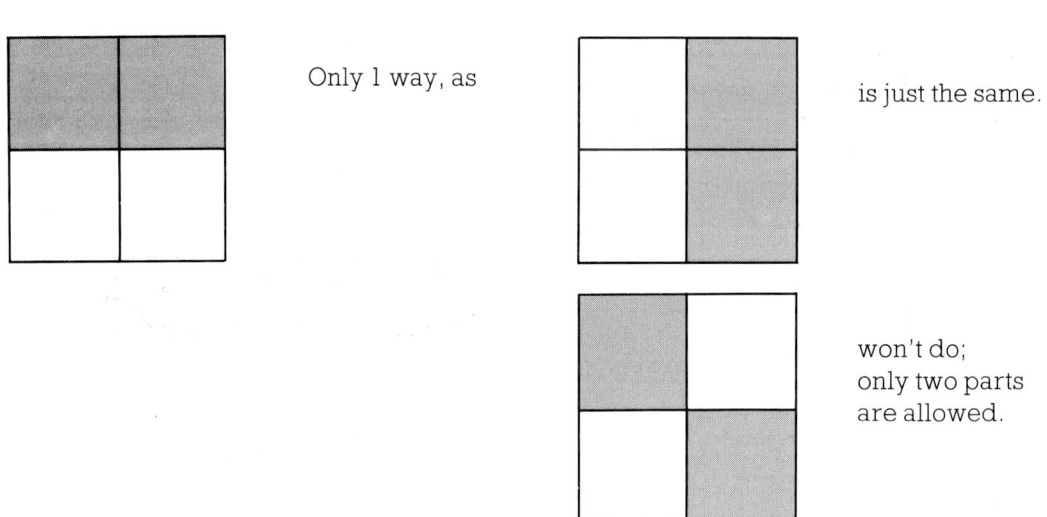

Only 1 way, as ... is just the same.

won't do; only two parts are allowed.

3 by 2 field

1 Explain why these are the only two possibilities.

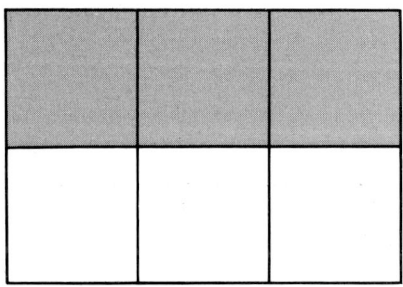 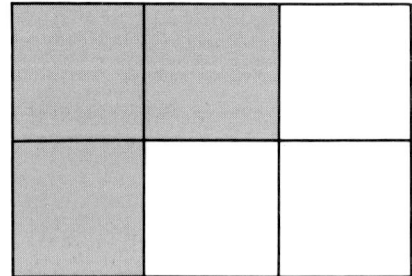

2 Investigate ways of splitting: 3×3, 4×2, 5×2, 4×3 and 4×4 fields.

3 Investigate ways in which 3 sisters can split 3×3 and 3×4 fields.

A magic square

Start with the Instruction Square, and use the values of a, b, and c to copy and complete the Magic Square.

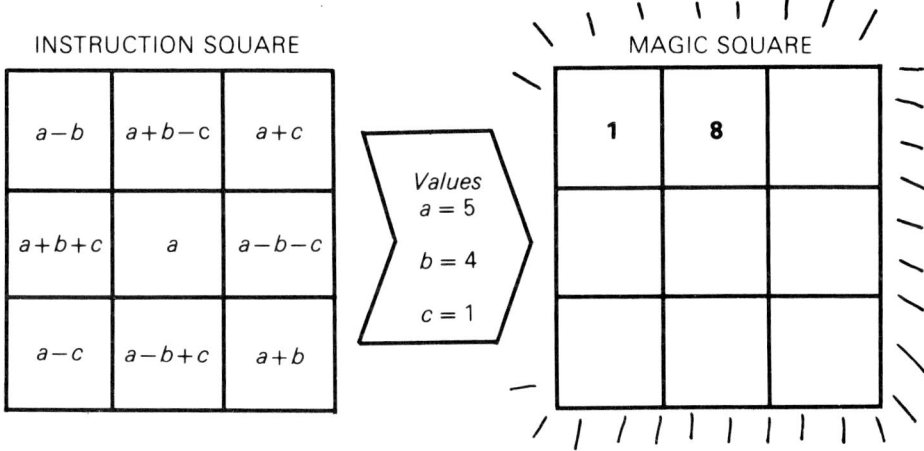

INSTRUCTION SQUARE

$a-b$	$a+b-c$	$a+c$
$a+b+c$	a	$a-b-c$
$a-c$	$a-b+c$	$a+b$

Values
$a = 5$
$b = 4$
$c = 1$

MAGIC SQUARE

1	8	

Check that the numbers in each row, column and diagonal add up to the same total.
Choose three different values for a, b and c. Investigate the row, column and diagonal totals, using the same instructions.
It always works, but why? Try adding the three algebraic expressions in a row, column and diagonal.

Model-car racing tracks

Grand Prix plc make model-car racing sets.
They make two different units of track, a 'straight' and a 45° 'curve'.

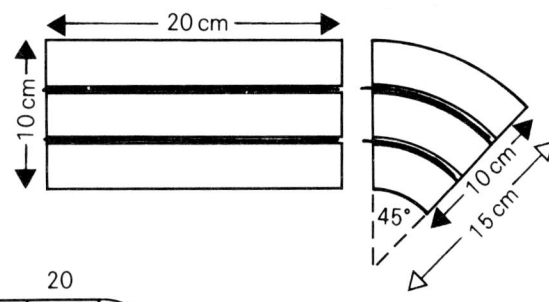

1 Their basic kit makes this circuit.

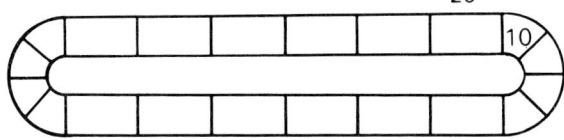

  a How many straights and curves are needed?
  b Make copies of these curves and straights from card, using a scale of 1:2 (so that a 'straight' will be 10 cm by 5 cm).
  c Design different circuits using this basic kit. Draw scaled-down copies of your designs.

2 Design larger circuits using more straights and curves.

3 Calculate the length right around the outer and inner edges of the basic kit circuit shown in **1**.

4 Investigate the prices of model-car racing layouts which are available in shops.

Multiplication table squares

×	1	2	3	4	5	6	7	8	9
1	1	2	3	4	5	6	7	8	9
2	2	4	6	8	10	12	14	16	18
3	3	6	9	12	15	18	21	24	27
4	4	8	12	16	20	24	28	32	36
5	5	10	15	20	25	30	35	40	45
6	6	12	18	24	30	36	42	48	54
7	7	14	21	28	35	42	49	56	63
8	8	16	24	32	40	48	56	64	72
9	9	18	27	36	45	54	63	72	81

Adrian studies a multiplication table.
He draws a square around four numbers.

1 a 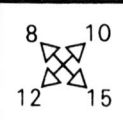 He *adds* diagonally opposite numbers.
What does he find?

Try more squares in other parts of the table.

b 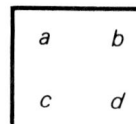 Here is any square in the table.
Copy and complete: $a + d = \ldots$

2 a 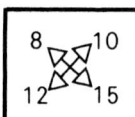 This time Adrian *multiplies* opposite numbers.
What does he find?

Try more squares in other parts of the table.
Using the letters in **1 b**, copy and complete: $ad = \ldots$

b 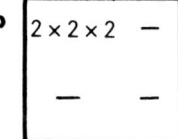 He writes 8 as $2 \times 2 \times 2$, using prime factors of 8.
Do the same for 10, 12, 15.

Show the multiplication of diagonals in full $2 \times 2 \times 2 \times \ldots \times \ldots = \ldots$
What do you find? Try this for other squares in the table.

3 a Which line of numbers is a line of symmetry of the numbers in the table?
b What do you notice about all of the numbers in this line?

Dinkie's bone

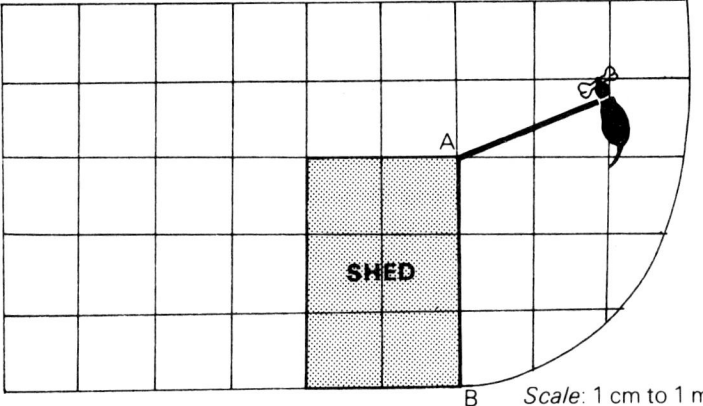

Scale: 1 cm to 1 m

The diagram shows Dinkie the dog's garden. The end of Dinkie's 2 metre long lead is tied to the garden shed at A.

1 a Copy the diagram and shade the area Dinkie can reach to bury the bone.
  b Repeat **a** for a lead of length: (i) 3 m   (ii) 4 m   (iii) 5 m.
  c Dinkie would like to reach the whole garden. How long would the lead have to be?

2 Repeat question **1** if the lead is tied at B instead of A.

3 Which point on the edge of the shed should the lead be fixed to for Dinkie to reach the whole garden with the shortest possible lead?

Egg sizes

This is a topic to try at home!

Size	Weight (g)
1	70 and over
2	65–69
3	60–64
4	55–59
5	50–54
6	45–49
7	under 45

Eggs are graded by weight.
1 Carefully check some eggs to see if they have been graded correctly.

2 Could eggs be graded by measuring the distances around them?
Design a grading system based on these lengths, either separately or added together.

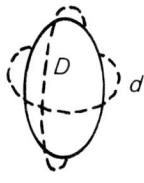

3 Can you find a connection between the distances around the eggs and their weights? A graph might help.

How many routes?

1

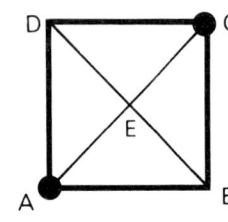

Routes from A to C
a Using 2 roads, A → E → C
                  A → B → C
Can you find another?
b Using 3 roads, A → B → E → C is one possibility.
Find others. (A road must not be used twice on any journey.)
c Continue the investigation for: (i) 4 roads (ii) 5 roads.

2

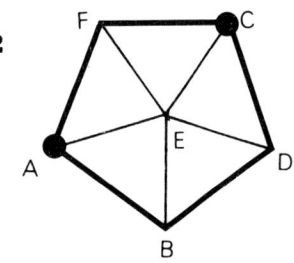

Repeat **1** for the pentagonal network of roads on the left.

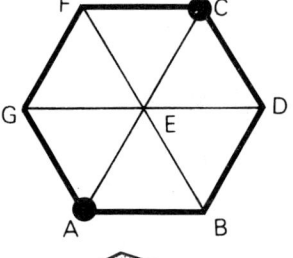

3 Repeat **1** for this hexagonal network of roads.

Building a brick wall

1 Terry and Jean want to build a brick wall about 10 m long, 1 m high and of 1 brick thickness alongside their garden. They know the size of a standard brick:

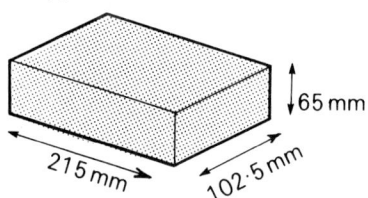

A 10 mm layer of mortar is put between bricks, so how many bricks will they need in a row, and how many rows for the wall?

How many bricks should they order?

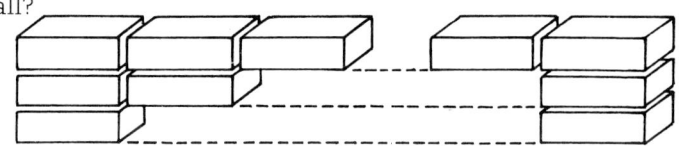

2 One sturdy brick wall design is called 'English bonding'.

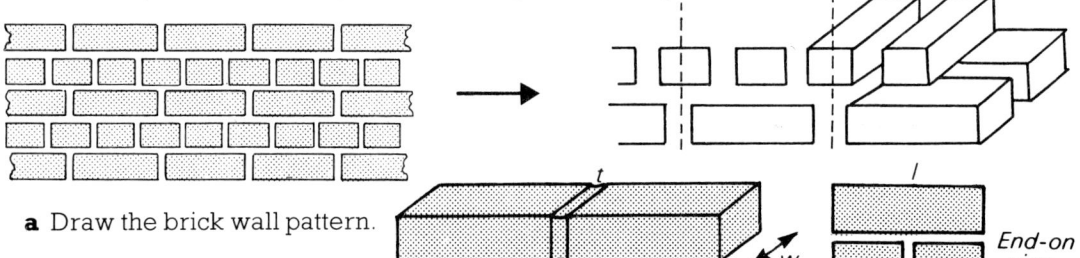

a Draw the brick wall pattern.
b Write down a formula connecting *l*, *w* and *t*.
c Use your formula to calculate the:
(i) length of a brick 120 mm wide ($t = 10$) (ii) width of a brick 275 mm long ($t = 10$).

d

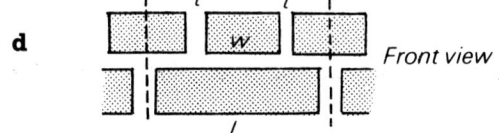

Front view

Is your formula true for this front view of the wall?

Tossing a coin

1 coin
Number of ways of landing a 'Head' = 1
Number of ways of landing no Heads (a 'Tail') = 1

2 coins

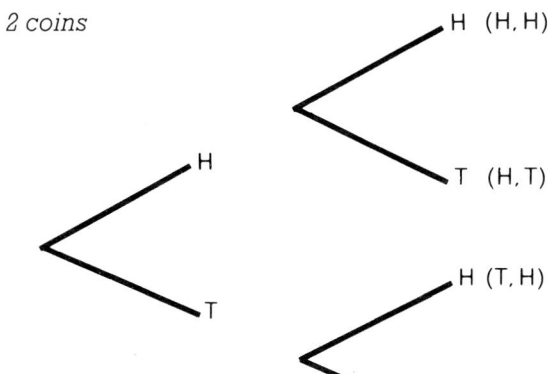

No. of ways of landing 2 Heads = 1
No. of ways of landing 1 Head = 2
No. of ways of landing 0 Heads = 1

3 coins

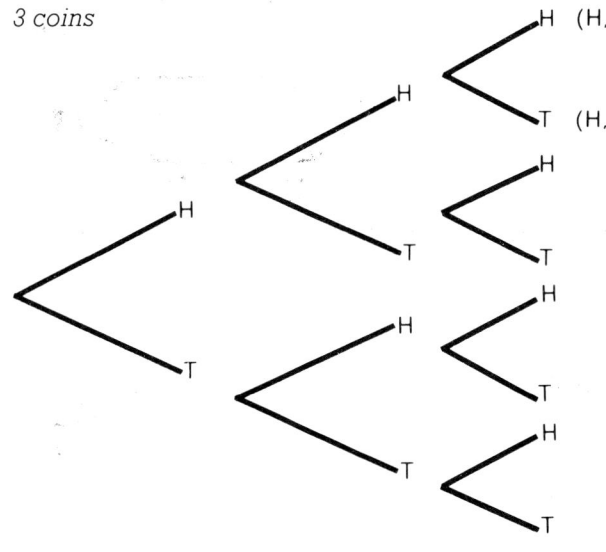

a Copy and complete the list of possibilities: HHH, HHT, . . .
b Copy and complete:
No. of ways of landing 3 Heads = 1
No. of ways of landing 2 Heads = 3
No. of ways of landing 1 Head = . . .
No. of ways of landing 0 Heads = . . .

c What is the connection between the above results and 'Pascal's Triangle'?

```
        1
      1   1
    1   2   1
  1   3   3   1
```

d Copy the triangle, and fill in the next three rows.
e Calculate: (i) P (HH) for 2 coins   (ii) P (HHH) for 3 coins
         (iii) P (HHH . . .) for 4, 5, 6, . . ., n coins.

Garages and greenhouses to order

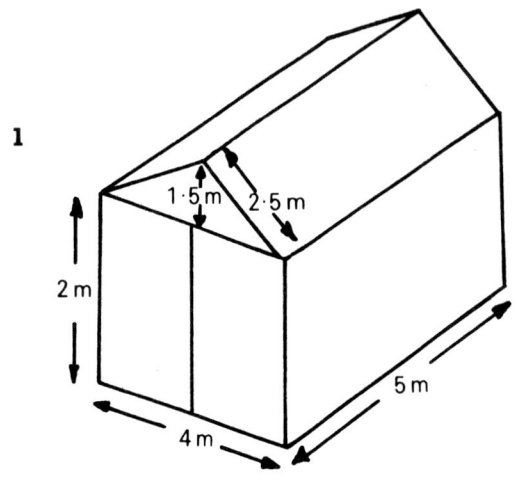

1

Kits cost £6 a square metre of surface area.
A concrete base costs £15 a square metre.
a Sketch each part of the kit.
b Calculate the area of each part.
c Calculate the cost of the kit and the base.

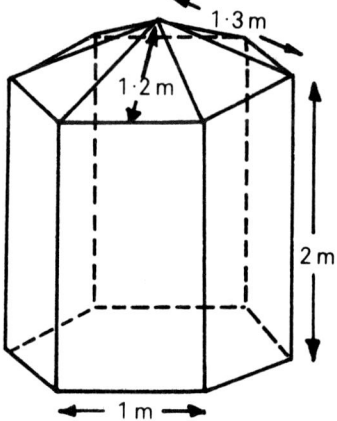

2 The same firm advertises kits for greenhouses like this
one. The base is a regular hexagon, and the framework
is made of aluminium strips which the glass slots into.
a Sketch a side panel and a roof panel.
b List the number and sizes of aluminium strips and
panes of glass in the kit.
c Calculate the total area of glass needed.

3 Design a garden hut which the firm might be interested in selling. Detail its dimensions and
the materials needed.

The Big Wheel

The Big Wheel has a radius
of 6 metres, and turns
through 10° each second.
Renita gets on at A, and
3 seconds later is at B, where
∠AOB = 30°.

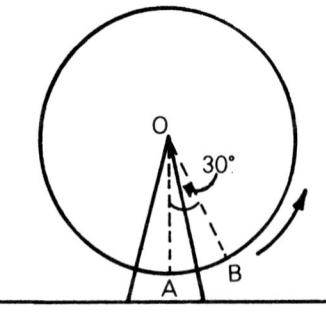

1 a Taking a scale of 1 cm to 1 m, make a scale drawing of the circular part of the Wheel.
  b Mark Renita's position every 3 seconds until she returns to A.

c *Measure* Renita's distance from A at each point, and copy and complete:

Angle turned through ($a°$)	0°	30°	60°	... ...	330°	360°
Distance from A (d metres)				...		

2 Draw a graph of d against a on 2 mm squared paper.
Do you recognise the graph? Parabola, hyperbola, sine wave, . . .?

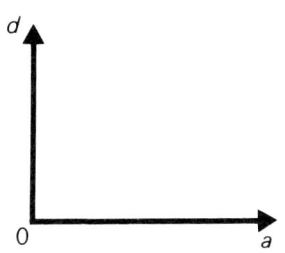

Sporting competitions

1 *Leagues*

a In the All-action league each team plays every other team twice (home and away). How many games are played altogether when there are:
(i) 2   (ii) 3   (iii) 4   (iv) 5   (v) 10 teams?

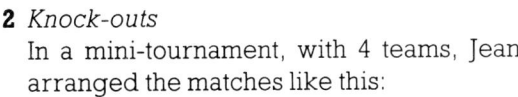

Suggestions. List all the fixtures *or* use a table

	Team		
	A	B	C
A	×	✓	✓
Team B			
C			

b Does the rule 'For n teams, calculate $n(n-1)$' work for each of your answers in **a**? How many games are played in English League Division I football fixtures for 21 teams?

2 *Knock-outs*
In a mini-tournament, with 4 teams, Jean arranged the matches like this:

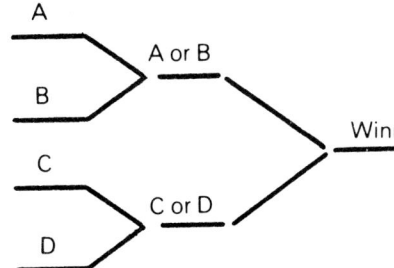

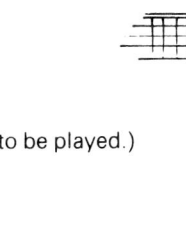

Winner (3 games to be played.)

a How many games have to be played in a knock-out competition for:
(i) 8   (ii) 16   (iii) 32   (iv) n, teams?
b What happens if the number of teams is not a power of 2, for example 7, or 19?

3

Choose your own sport, number of teams and type of competition. Work out a fixture list and competition plan, and calculate the number of games to be played.

The Dambusters

To bounce along the surface and hit the wall of the dam, the 'bouncing bomb' had to be dropped at exactly the right height above the water. Here is how it was done.

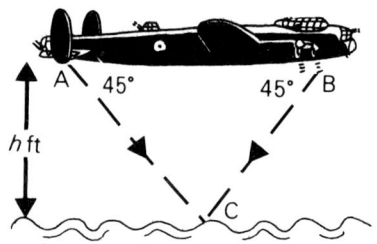

Spotlights were fitted to the Lancaster bombers at two points A and B. The beams of light were aimed so that they met at C on the surface of the water when the height h feet of the plane was exactly right.

1 If AB = 60 feet, find h.

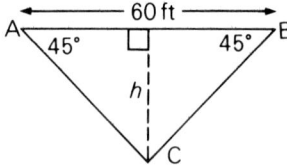

2 Use trigonometry or a scale drawing to find:
a h if the angle between each beam and the aircraft was 65°
b the angle between each beam and the aircraft if h had to be 100.

3 The navigator sees two spots of light on the water 20 feet apart, when each beam was set at 45° to the aircraft. Find the height of the aircraft above the water. Is there more than one possible answer?

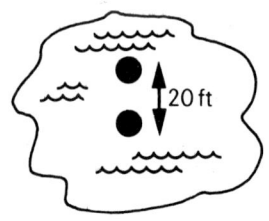

Barn buildings

Apex Architects specialise in farm buildings. Before designing new barns they have to calculate the sum of the angles in the cross-section.

1 Copy and complete:

	Number of Sides	Number of Triangles	Sum of Angles
Quadrilateral 	4	2	$2 \times 180°$
Pentagon 	. . .	. . .	$\ldots \times 180°$
Hexagon . . .	. . .	. . .	$\ldots \times 180°$
n-gon . . .	. . .	. . .	$\ldots \times 180°$

2 The cross-section of the Architects' first barn looks like this:
a Show that $x + x + 2x + 2x = 360$.
b Calculate x.

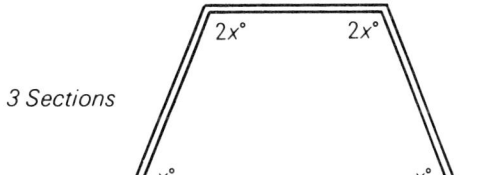

3 Sections

3 They add another section:
Make an equation, and find x.

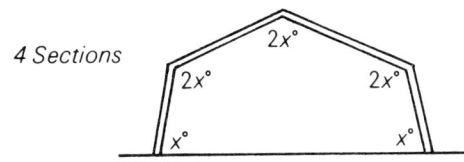

4 Sections

4 They add another section:
Make an equation, and find x.

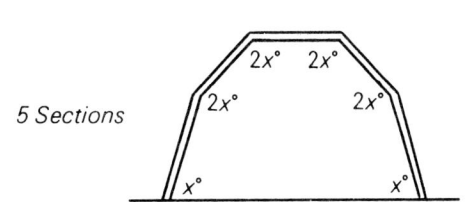

5 Sections

5 Copy and complete:

Number of sections	3	4	5	6	7
x					

6 Show that the formula $x = 90 - \dfrac{90}{n}$, where n is the number of sections, works for $n = 3, 4, \ldots, 7$.

7 Calculate x for: **a** 18 sections **b** 30 sections.

A concrete jungle

Mr and Mrs Primrose have a *square* garden 10 m long. Mr Primrose wants to pave it all over to avoid the digging and weeding.
Mrs Primrose wants to have it all under flowers and herbs.
A compromise is reached. Mr Primrose can pave part of the garden by making a path of uniform width round the inside edge.

1 They decide that the area of the plot in the middle will be $\frac{1}{4}$ of the area of the whole garden.

Calculate: **a** the area of the plot in the middle   **b** the length of side of this plot
            c the width of the path.

2 Mr Primrose insists on trying some other fractions for the area of the plot. Repeat the calculations in question **1** when the area of the plot is:
(i) $\frac{1}{2}$ (ii) $\frac{1}{3}$ (iii) $\frac{1}{5}$ of the area of the garden.
Give your answers correct to 2 significant figures.

Mathematics results at Park High School

Here are Park's GCSE results in Mathematics for the last two sessions.
The session before last:

Grade	A	B	C	D	E	F	G	U	Did not take exam	TOTAL
Number of pupils	18	19	30	47	51	25	15	11	24	240

Last session:

Grade	A	B	C	D	E	F	G	U	Did not take exam	TOTAL
Number of pupils	17	16	30	42	36	24	11	16	10	202

(U = unclassified)

1 Draw bar graphs of the two sessions' results.

2 a Calculate the percentage of passes at each grade the session before last.

For example, *Grade A*: $\frac{18}{240} \times 100\% = 7 \cdot 5\%$.   Put your answers in a table.

b Repeat for last session's results.

3 For each session, write down: (i) the mode (ii) the median grade.

4 This session's results have just arrived, and are listed below:

EAEEFCUEFG	EDCGCBFEAD
GECGDDFDED	EUEDEFDEEA
EDEAFBUBDF	DDGCE
DAEEDECFDC	EEFCAGABAE
CUABDDDFFD	EGCDBDUCFB
UEDABAEFDE	AEDFEGBADF
DAEEFGAFBD	CAEAGCGCGD
DDEDFCDFFF	FDDUCAEDFB
CGAEFCEBDG	GBCBEDEFBB

Two pupils did not take the exam.
The Headmaster has asked you, as Head of Mathematics, to prepare a report containing

a an analysis of this session's results

b a pictorial or graphical presentation of the three sessions' results

c a comparison of results year by year, with comments on any changes.

The Stocks and Shares game

Play this on your own, or with a group of friends

1 *On your own* You have £500 to invest in shares.

a Choose five well-known companies listed on the financial page of a daily newspaper. Note the price of their shares, and decide how many shares you will buy in each company. Fill in copies of the Buying Form and the Value Form.

b Each week (or month) you may buy or sell shares at the prices quoted in the newspaper, and complete copies of the Selling Form and the Value Form.

c Keep the forms, and make a graphical record of the performance of your shares over a term. Write a Report on their (and your) performance.

2 *In a group* Each player starts with £500.

Ask the teacher to select five companies. Then proceed as in **1** above.

BUYING FORM

ROUND No. [ ]   DATE [_____]

INVESTOR [_____|___]

	A PRICE	G No. HELD	J No. BOUGHT	EXPENDITURE (A × J)	K NEW No. HELD (G + J)
Company No. 1 _____	[ ]	[ ]	[ ]	[ ]	[ ]
Company No. 2 _____	[ ]	[ ]	[ ]	[ ]	[ ]
Company No. 3 _____	[ ]	[ ]	[ ]	[ ]	[ ]
Company No. 4 _____	[ ]	[ ]	[ ]	[ ]	[ ]
Company No. 5 _____	[ ]	[ ]	[ ]	[ ]	[ ]

SPARE CASH [I]   TOTAL EXPENDITURE [L]

NEW SPARE CASH [_____]
(I – L)

◄ Transfer to Box D on new Value form

Transfer to column B on new Value form

VALUE FORM

ROUND No. [ ]   DATE [_____]

INVESTOR (NAME AND No.) [_____|___]

	A PRICE	B No. HELD	C VALUE (A × B)
Company No. 1 _____	[ ]	[ ]	[ ]
Company No. 2 _____	[ ]	[ ]	[ ]
Company No. 3 _____	[ ]	[ ]	[ ]
Company No. 4 _____	[ ]	[ ]	[ ]
Company No. 5 _____	[ ]	[ ]	[ ]

SPARE CASH [D]   PRESENT VALUE OF SHARES [E]

PRESENT TOTAL VALUE OF INVESTMENT [_____]
(D + E)

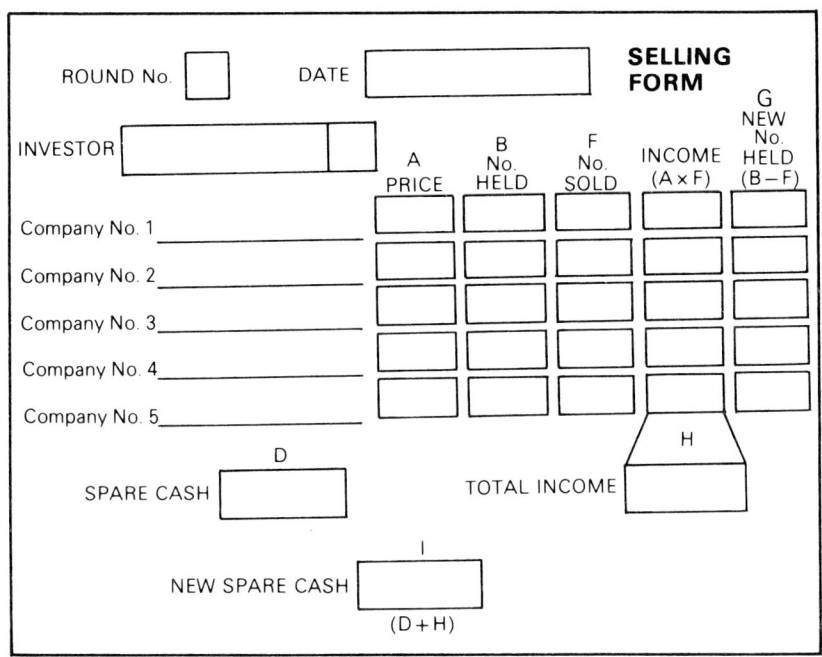

ROUND No. [ ]   DATE [   ]   **SELLING FORM**

INVESTOR [ ][ ]	A PRICE	B No. HELD	F No. SOLD	INCOME (A × F)	G NEW No. HELD (B − F)
Company No. 1 _____	[ ]	[ ]	[ ]	[ ]	[ ]
Company No. 2 _____	[ ]	[ ]	[ ]	[ ]	[ ]
Company No. 3 _____	[ ]	[ ]	[ ]	[ ]	[ ]
Company No. 4 _____	[ ]	[ ]	[ ]	[ ]	[ ]
Company No. 5 _____	[ ]	[ ]	[ ]	[ ]	[ ]

SPARE CASH D [   ]   TOTAL INCOME H [   ]

NEW SPARE CASH I [   ]
(D + H)

Resistor colour codes

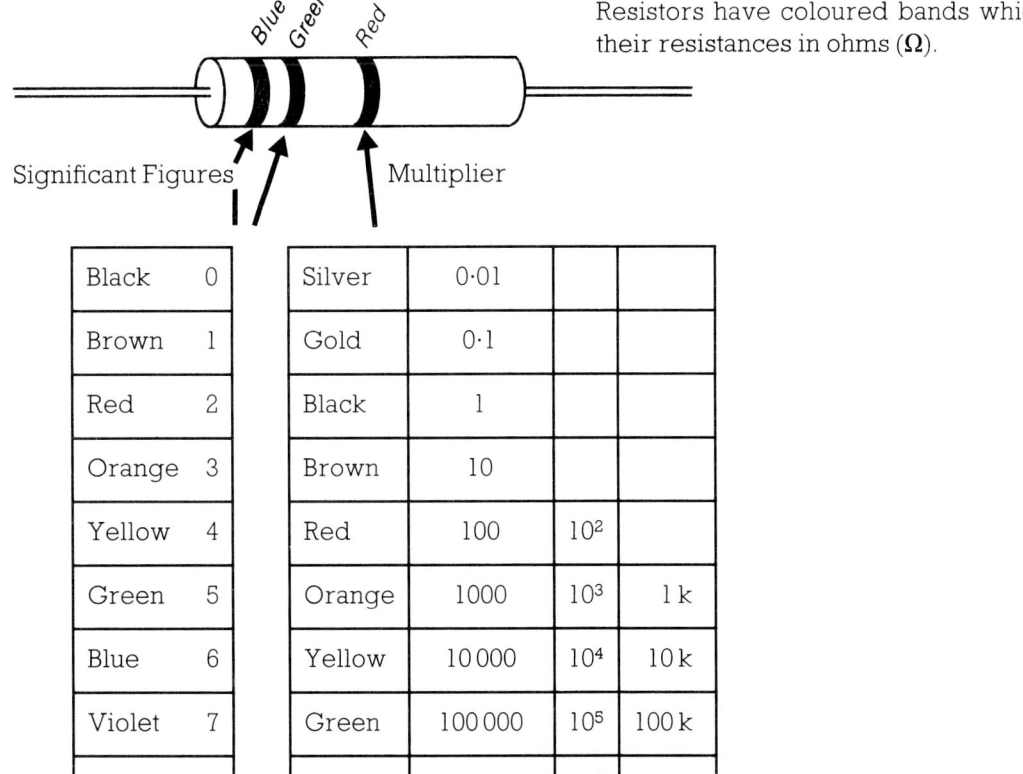

Blue Green   Red

Significant Figures   Multiplier

Resistors have coloured bands which show their resistances in ohms (Ω).

Black	0		Silver	0·01		
Brown	1		Gold	0·1		
Red	2		Black	1		
Orange	3		Brown	10		
Yellow	4		Red	100	10^2	
Green	5		Orange	1000	10^3	1 k
Blue	6		Yellow	10 000	10^4	10 k
Violet	7		Green	100 000	10^5	100 k
Grey	8		Blue	1 000 000	10^6	1 m
White	9		Violet	10 000 000	10^7	10 m

The first bands give the significant figures; the last one gives the multiplier. For example, for the resistor on page 31:

Band 1   Band 2   Multiplier
Blue = 6   Green = 5   Red = 100

The resistance is $65 \times 100 = 6500\,\Omega = 6.5\,k\Omega$

Examples

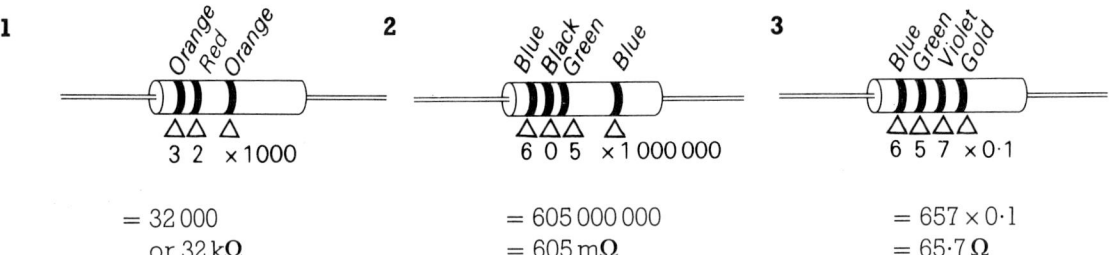

1
Orange Red Orange
3 2   × 1000

= 32 000
or 32 kΩ

2
Blue Black Green Blue
6 0 5   × 1 000 000

= 605 000 000
= 605 mΩ

3
Blue Green Violet Gold
6 5 7   × 0·1

= 657 × 0·1
= 65·7 Ω

1 Calculate these resistances:

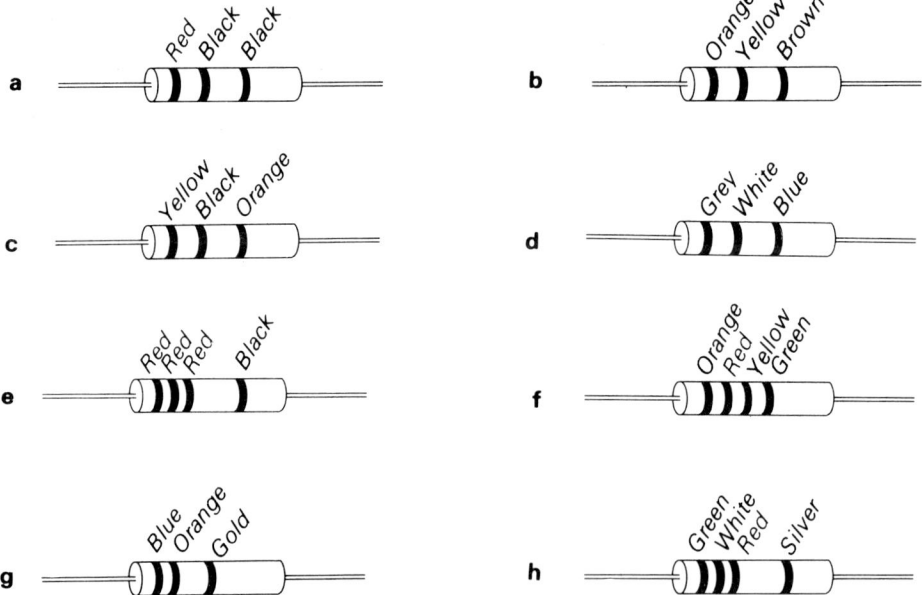

a   Red Black Black

b   Orange Yellow Brown

c   Yellow Black Orange

d   Grey White Blue

e   Red Red Red Black

f   Orange Red Yellow Green

g   Blue Orange Gold

h   Green White Red Silver

2 Draw resistors with these resistances, showing the colour of their bands:
   a 26 Ω   **b** 560 Ω   **c** 3300 Ω   **d** 79 kΩ
   e 78 mΩ   **f** 3·4 Ω   **g** 0·50 Ω   **h** 0·063 Ω

3 Ask a Science or Technology teacher if you can see some resistors. Work out their resistances.

Grid line lengths

1 by 1 grid
Sue can draw two straight lines of different lengths, which join points on a 1 by 1 grid:

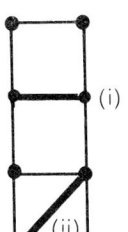

Line (i) is 1 unit long.
Using Pythagoras' Theorem, Sue calculates that the length of line (ii) is $\sqrt{2}$.

1 Show how Sue does this.

2 by 2 grid

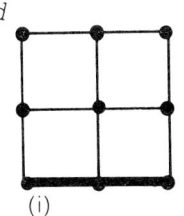 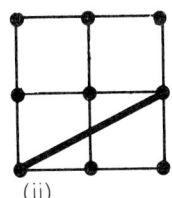 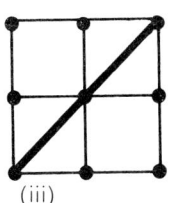

Sue finds 3 new lengths on this grid.

2 Show that their lengths are 2, $\sqrt{5}$ and $\sqrt{8}$.

3 Draw a 3 by 3 grid and find all possible new lengths.

4 a Start a table like this:

Grid Size	New Lengths	Total Number of Lengths
1 by 1	1, $\sqrt{2}$	2
2 by 2	2, $\sqrt{5}$, $\sqrt{8}$	2 + 3 = 5
3 by 3	3,	

b Continue the investigation for larger grids.

5 Using $\sqrt{1}$ (1), $\sqrt{2}$, $\sqrt{3}$, $\sqrt{4}$ (2), ..., list all the lengths up to $\sqrt{50}$ it is possible to find.

Combining cubes

1 *3 cubes*
   a Use 3 cubes to make these shapes (use a different colour for each shape).

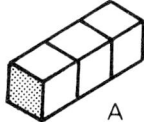 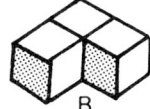

   b Are these all the possible shapes?

2 *4 cubes*
  a Use 4 cubes to make these shapes (use a different colour for each shape).

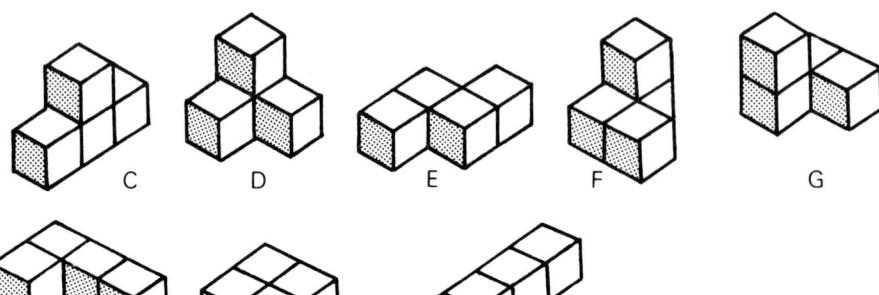

C   D   E   F   G

H   I   J

b Are these all the possible shapes?

3 *To make a 3 by 3 by 3 cube*
  Select either A or B, and *all but one* of C, D, E, F, G, H, I. (Type J is not used here.)
  a How many small cubes do you have in your selection?
  b Are there enough to make a 3 by 3 by 3 cube? Explain.

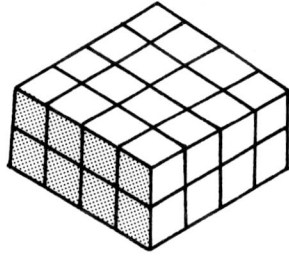

  c Use your selection to make a 3 by 3 by 3 cube.
  d Investigate different selections.

4 Use C, D, E, F, G, H, I and J to make a 4 by 4 by 2 cuboid.

5 What other cuboids can you make with your shapes?

When will we meet again?

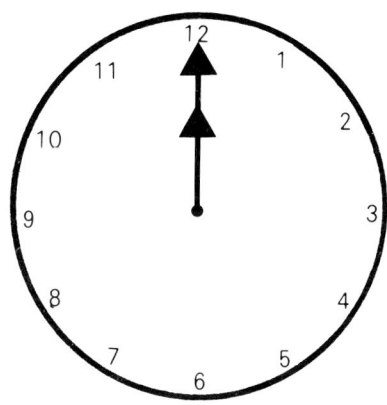

At 12 o'clock the hour hand and the minute hand point in the same direction.
Anne and Claire try to work out when this will next happen.

1 They work out that the minute hand turns through 6° per minute, and that the hour hand turns through 0·5° per minute.

a Show how they do this.

Anne says the hands will meet just after 1 o'clock. She makes a table of the degrees turned from 1 p.m.

b Copy and complete the table

Time		1.00	1.01	1.02	1.03	1.04	1.05	1.06
Degrees turned from top	Minute hand	0	6	12	18			
	Hour hand	30°	30·5°	31°				

c Draw a graph on 2 mm squared paper, showing the degrees turned by each hand between 1.00 and 1.06 p.m.

d At what time do they meet?

2 Claire tries to be more accurate. From Anne's graph she sees that the hands meet between *5 and 6 minutes past one*.

She makes a table of the angles turned through by the hands at 1.05 and 1.06 p.m.

a Copy and complete the table:

Time		1.05	1.06
Degrees turned	Minute hand	30°	
	Hour hand	32·5°	

b Draw a graph for each hand.
c When do they meet (to the nearest second)?

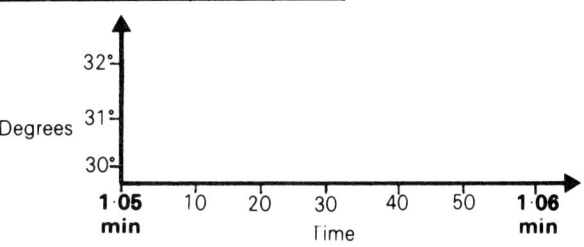

Car brakes

Evan's car is in for its MOT test. Its brakes are tested on a roller. The rules are:

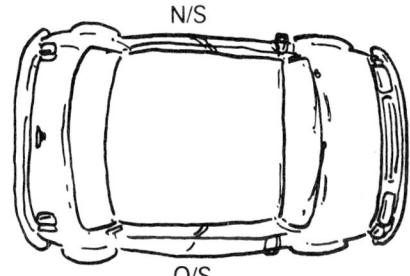

(i) the foot brake must be at least 75% efficient
(ii) the handbrake must be at least 25% efficient.
(iii) the braking effect of one front wheel must be at least 75% of that of the other front wheel.

Here are the results for Evan's car:
(N/S means near-side, i.e. near-pavement side, and O/S means off-side.)

Foot brake (kg)	*Hand brake*(kg) (acts on rear wheels only)
Front N/S = 400	N/S 170
Front O/S = 300	O/S 130
Rear N/S = 120	⎯⎯
Rear O/S = 110	300
⎯⎯	⎯⎯
930	
⎯⎯	

Weight of car = 1200 kg

(i) Foot brake efficiency $= \dfrac{930}{1200} \times 100 = 77.5\%$

(ii) Hand brake efficiency $= \dfrac{300}{1200} \times 100 = 25\%$

(iii) Front wheel balance efficiency $= \dfrac{300}{400} \times 100 = 75\%$ Does Evan's car pass all three tests?

1 Which of these cars would pass all three tests? In the case of failure, explain what the fault is. (Hand brake readings are in brackets.)

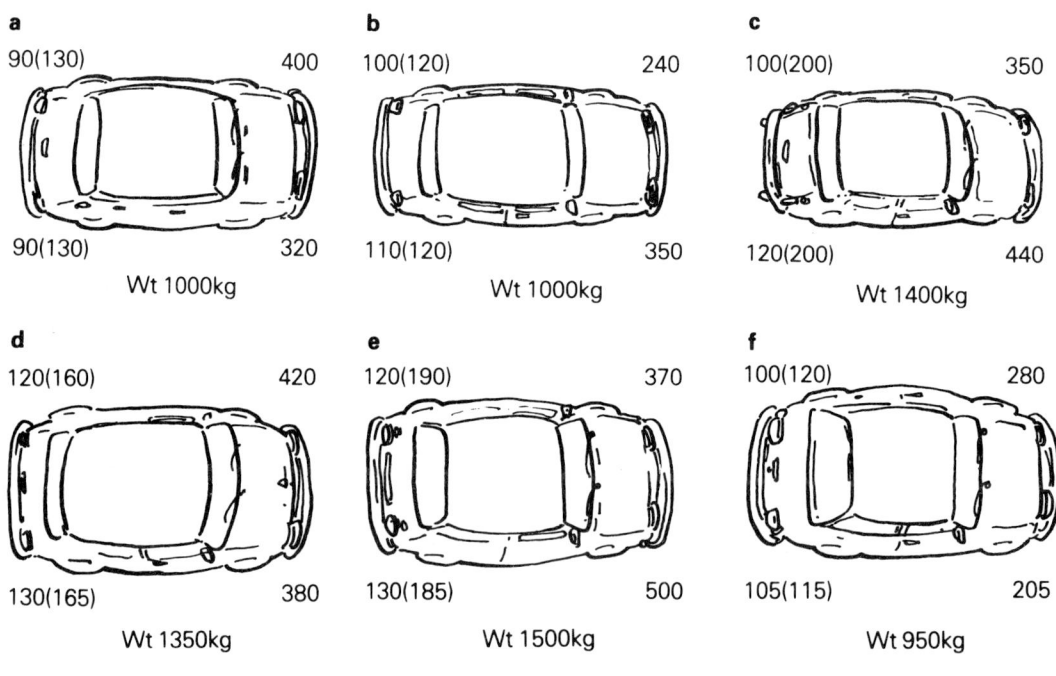

a
90(130)   400

90(130)   320
Wt 1000kg

b
100(120)   240

110(120)   350
Wt 1000kg

c
100(200)   350

120(200)   440
Wt 1400kg

d
120(160)   420

130(165)   380
Wt 1350kg

e
120(190)   370

130(185)   500
Wt 1500kg

f
100(120)   280

105(115)   205
Wt 950kg

2 a What does each test do, and why is it important?
   b Why is the weight of the car important?
   c Why are the front brakes more effective than the rear brakes?

3 Marie's car weighs 1250 kg.
   a Design a set of figures which would just pass the three tests.
   b Change the figures in three different ways to fail each test.

Atoms and molecules

1 The most common ways in which metallic atoms are arranged in crystals are shown below.

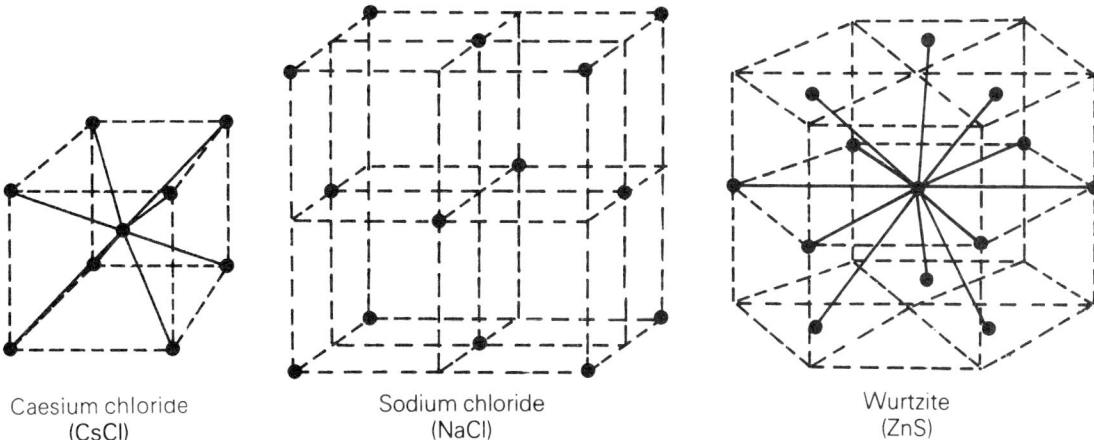

Caesium chloride
(CsCl)

Sodium chloride
(NaCl)

Wurtzite
(ZnS)

Study the dotted line structures to see how the atoms are arranged. Make a model of one of them. Notice all the planes of symmetry. Calculate some of the angles between the atoms.

2 In molecules, pairs of electrons are situated around a central atom.

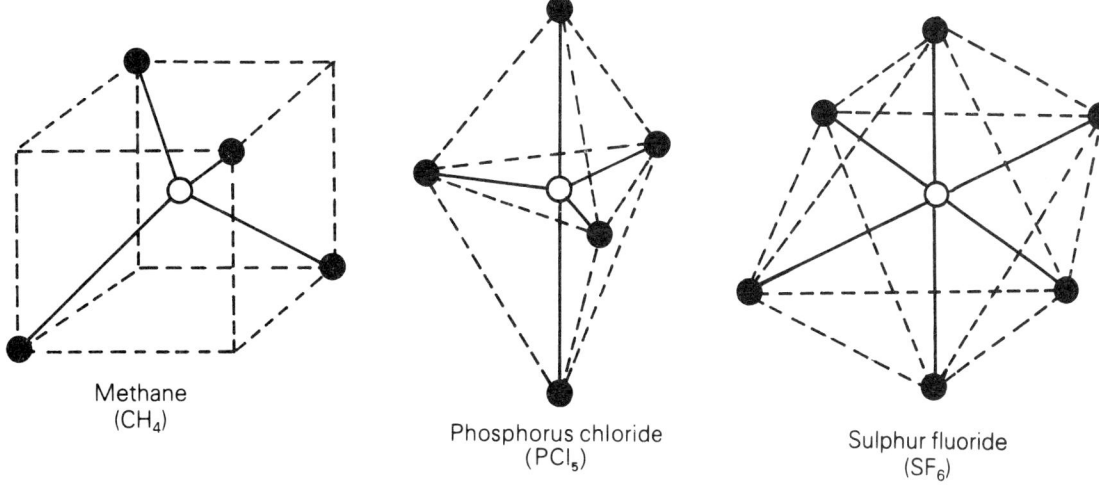

Methane
(CH$_4$)

Phosphorus chloride
(PCl$_5$)

Sulphur fluoride
(SF$_6$)

Make a model of one of them. Describe its symmetries, relative dimensions and 'bond angles' between the central atom and the pairs of electrons at the vertices.

3 Investigate other crystallography models.

Splitting circles

1 Draw the two patterns.
Each diameter is divided into centimetres.

(i)

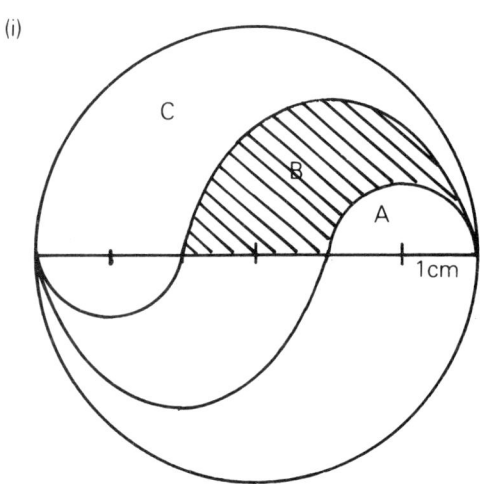

(ii)

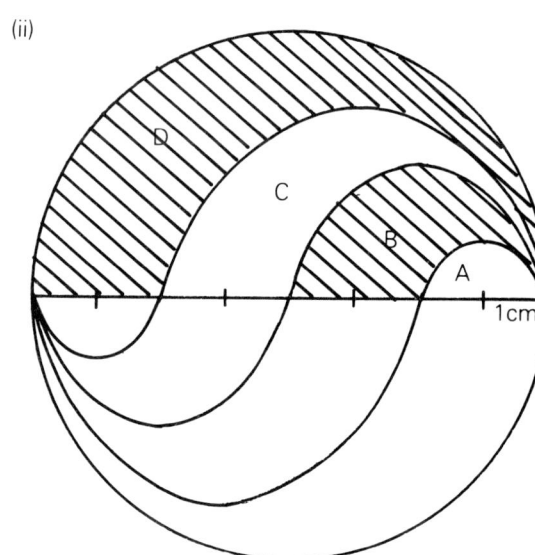

2 In (i), A, B and C are the areas of the three parts of the top half of the circle.
  a Show that $A = \frac{1}{2}\pi$, $B = 2\pi - \frac{1}{2}\pi = \frac{3}{2}\pi$ and $C = \frac{5}{2}\pi$.
  b Explain how this helps you to prove that the large circle is divided into three equal parts.
  c What fractions are A, B and C of the whole circle?

3 Repeat question **2** for circle (ii), and its parts A, B, C and D.

4 A circle is split into five equal parts. What fraction of the circle is the new area E?

5 A circle is split into n equal parts. What fraction of the circle is the new part at the top of the circle?

Number sequences

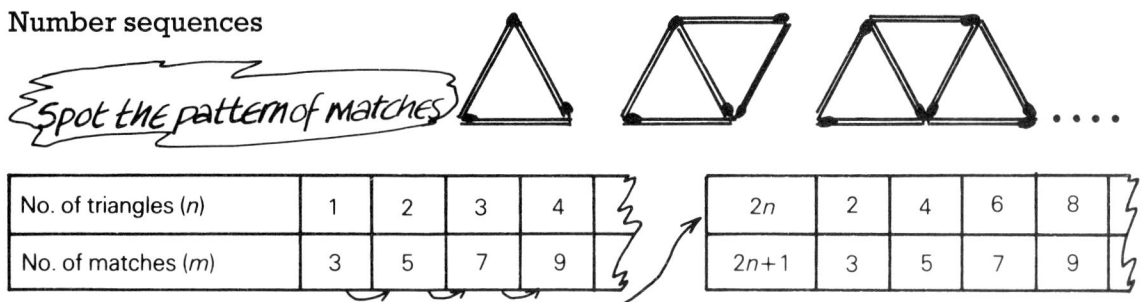

Spot the pattern of matches

No. of triangles (n)	1	2	3	4		$2n$	2	4	6	8
No. of matches (m)	3	5	7	9		$2n+1$	3	5	7	9

$+2$ $+2$ $+2$

The formula for m matches is $m = 2n+1$.

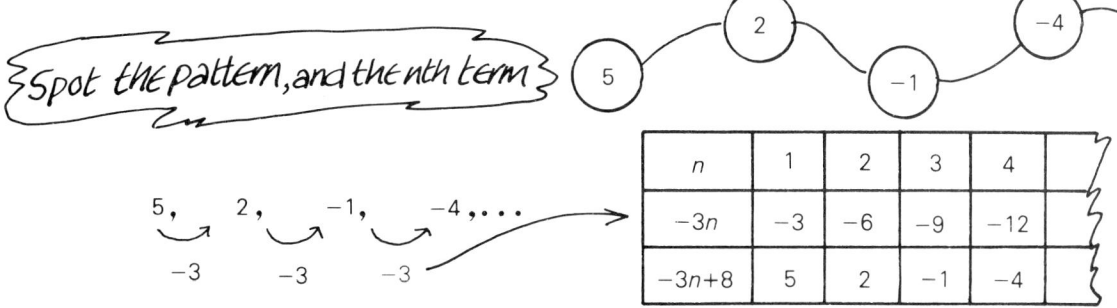

Spot the pattern, and the nth term

5, 2, -1, -4, . . .
  -3 -3 -3

n	1	2	3	4	
$-3n$	-3	-6	-9	-12	
$-3n+8$	5	2	-1	-4	

The formula for the nth term is $t_n = -3n+8$.
The 100th term is $t_{100} = -3 \times 100 + 8 = -300 + 8 = -292$.

> *Note* In this type of sequence, $t_n = an+b$, where a and b are numbers

1 Find a formula for t_n in each sequence. Check your formulae for $n = 1$ and $n = 2$.

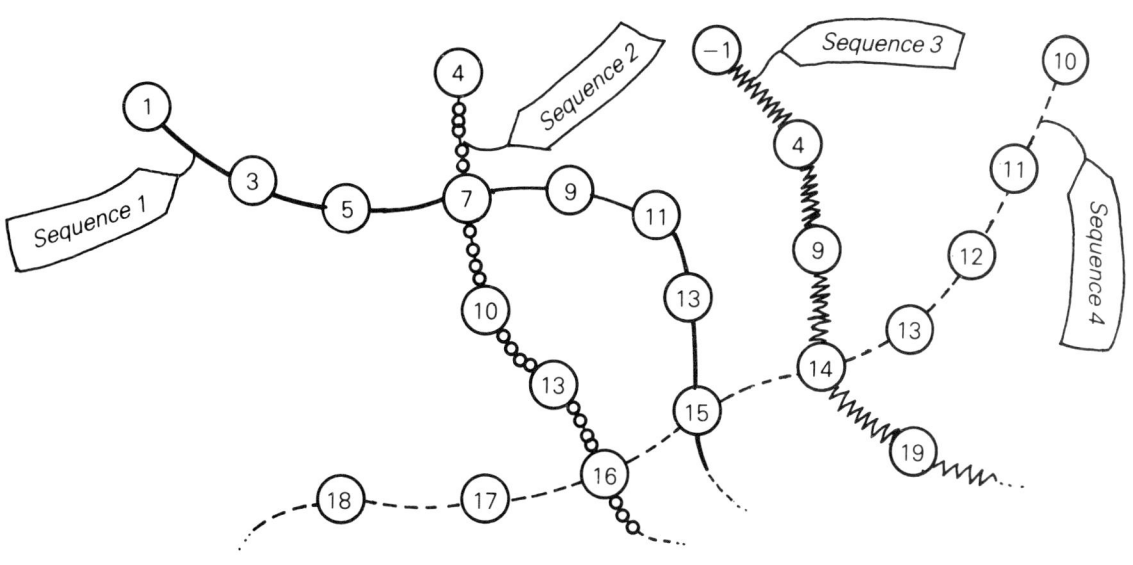

2 Find the 100th term in each of these sequences:
 a 2, 4, 6, 8, 10, . . .   **b** -1, 1, 3, 5, 7, . . .
 c 14, 12, 10, 8, 6, . . .   **d** -3, -7, -11, -15, -19, . . .

3 Copy and complete the table for the sequence of squares of matches:

Number of squares	1	2	3	4		n
Number of matches						
Perimeter						

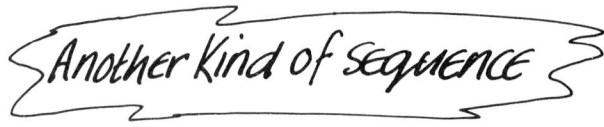

$$\underbrace{1 \quad 3 \quad 6 \quad 10 \quad 15}_{} \ldots t_n$$
$$+2 \ +3 \ +4 \quad +5$$
$$+1 \ +1 \ \ +1$$

> This time, $t_n = an^2 + bn + c$.

If $n = 1$, $\quad a + b + c = 1$
If $n = 2$, $\quad 4a + 2b + c = 3$ $\quad 3a + b = 2$
If $n = 3$, $\quad 9a + 3b + c = 6$ $\quad 5a + b = 3$ $\quad 2a = 1$, so $a = \frac{1}{2}$
Using $3a + b = 2$, $\quad b = \frac{1}{2}$.

Using $a + b + c = 1$, $\quad c = 0$. $\quad$ So $t_n = \frac{1}{2}n^2 + \frac{1}{2}n = \frac{1}{2}n(n+1)$

Check $\quad n = 1$, $\quad t_1 = \frac{1}{2} + \frac{1}{2} = 1$.

$\quad\quad\quad\quad n = 2$, $\quad t_2 = \frac{1}{2} \times 4 + \frac{1}{2} \times 2 = 3$, and so on.

4 Find a formula for t_n in each sequence. Check your formula for $n = 1$ and $n = 2$.

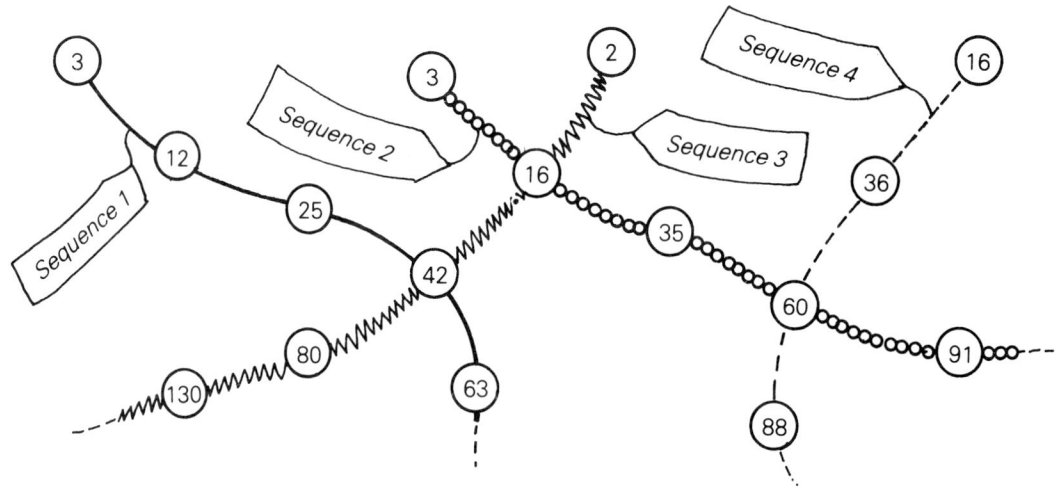

5 Find the nth term and the 100th term in each sequence:
   a 2, 6, 12, 20, 30, . . . $\quad\quad$ **b** 3, 8, 15, 24, 35, . . .
   c 1, 3, 8, 16, 27, 41, . . . $\quad$ **d** 2, 12, 24, 38, 54, . . .

6

Figure number	1	2	3	4		n
Number of small triangles	1	4				
Number of matches						
Extra number of matches						
No of triangles of all sizes						

Copy and complete the table for this sequence of matchstick triangles.

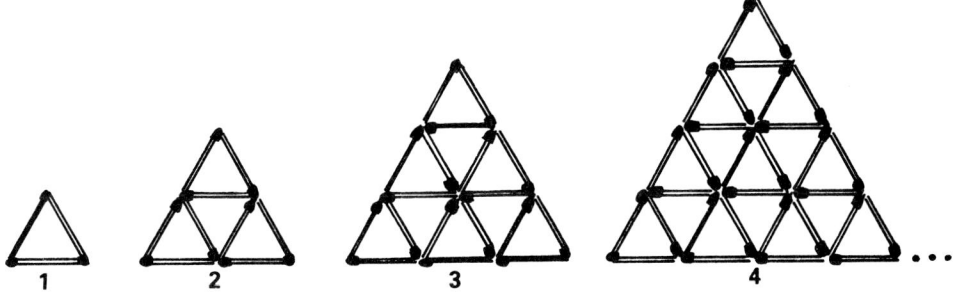

7 *Make your own sequences.* Form a product of two items, for example $n(2n+1)$.

$t_1 = 1(2+1) = 3$

$t_2 = 2(4+1) = 10$, and so on, making your sequence:

3 10 21 36 55...

Try to check 'backwards' from sequence to nth term, or ask a neighbour to try it.

SELF SERVICE

n	$n-1$	$2n$
$n+2$	$n-2$	$3n$
$n+3$	$2n+1$	$n+1$

8 *Some brainstormers.* Try to find the nth terms of:

a $1, 2, 4, 8, 16, \ldots$ **b** $2, 6, 18, 54, 162, \ldots$ **c** $1, -1, 1, -1, 1, \ldots$

A 'Head of Year' Election

The Fifth Year at City High are going to vote for a pupil to be their Head of Year. There are two candidates, Oliver and Belinda.

The week before the election Jane decides to carry out an opinion poll by asking 10 pupils how they intend to vote. There are six forms in the fifth year, each with 30 pupils, and she will take the poll while the pupils are in their form rooms. The diagram shows the pupils' voting intentions, O for Oliver and B for Belinda.

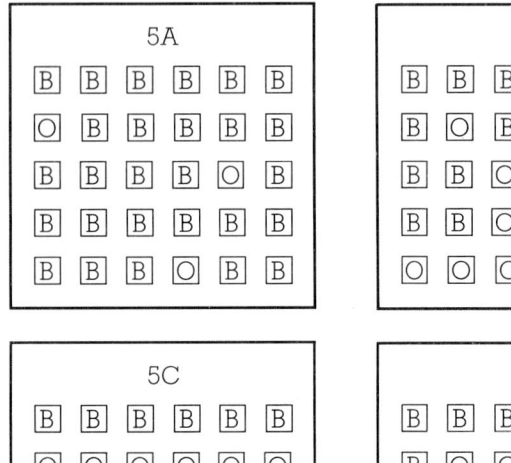

1 Jane has to select 10 pupils *at random* for her sample poll. Explain how she might do this. Select 10 random pupils, and list their places by giving their form, and the row and column of their desk, for example 5B, row 5, column 6.

2 Use your sample to predict the outcome of the election.

3 Repeat your method to select 10 different pupils. Compare your results.

4 Count all the votes, and compare the actual results with your polls.

5 Try your method, using a sample of 20 pupils. Are the results closer? Try samples of 30, 40, . . . pupils.

6 Real polls include a 'margin of error'. Can you estimate yours?

Launch rockets

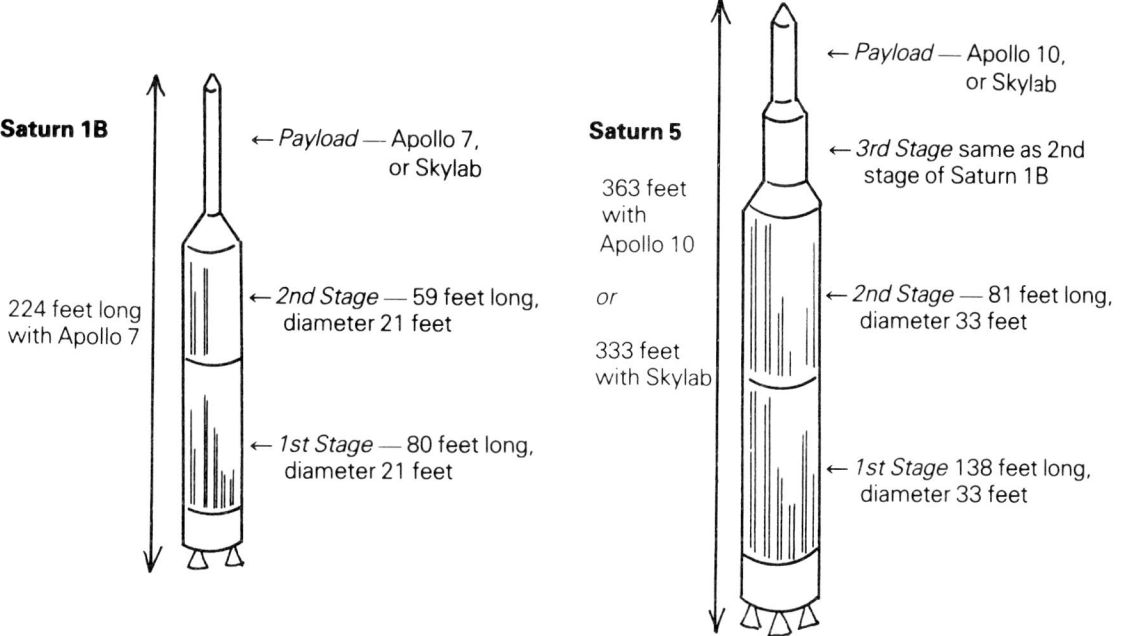

Saturn 1B

224 feet long
with Apollo 7

← *Payload* — Apollo 7,
or Skylab

← *2nd Stage* — 59 feet long,
diameter 21 feet

← *1st Stage* — 80 feet long,
diameter 21 feet

Saturn 5

363 feet
with
Apollo 10

or

333 feet
with Skylab

← *Payload* — Apollo 10,
or Skylab

← *3rd Stage* same as 2nd
stage of Saturn 1B

← *2nd Stage* — 81 feet long,
diameter 33 feet

← *1st Stage* 138 feet long,
diameter 33 feet

1 Make scale models of Saturn 1B and Saturn 5.

2 Calculate the volume and curved surface area of each stage of each rocket.

3 Use your answers in **2** and the scale for your models to calculate the volume and curved
surface area of each stage of each model rocket.

4 Apollo 10 reached a top speed of 24 790 mph on its way to the moon. Investigate:
  a the time the journey took   **b** the speeds and times of space missions to the planets.

5 Apollo 7 weighed 32 395 pounds. Investigate the weights of rockets and their payloads for
different space missions.

6 To be classed as a space flight a rocket, or aircraft, must achieve a height of 100 km
(62 miles). To get into orbit a satellite must reach a speed of mach 25, approximately.
Investigate other mathematical space facts and modern space missions and rockets.

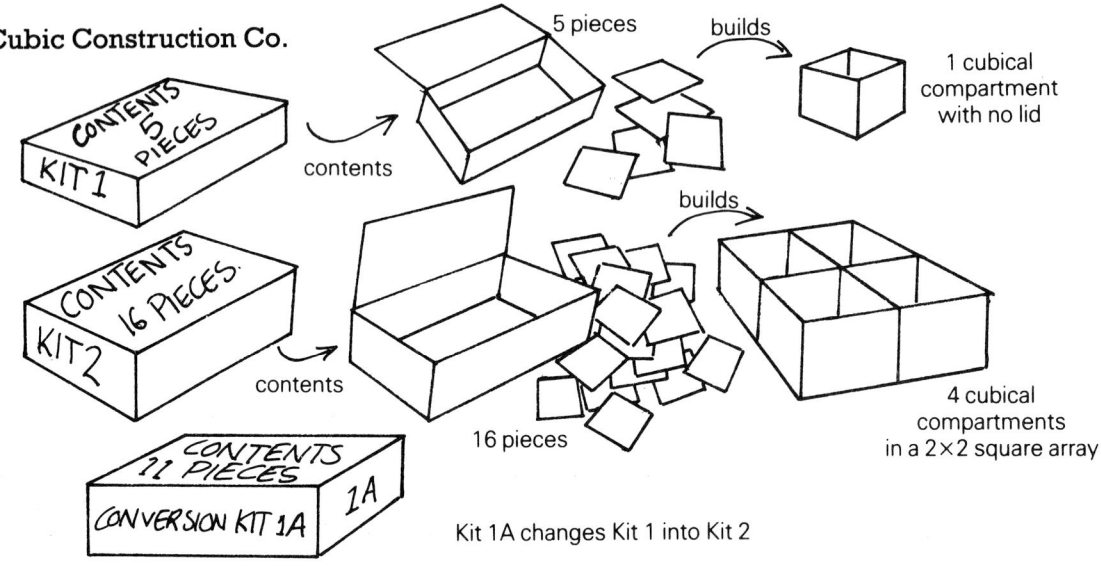

Cubic Construction Co.

5 pieces builds 1 cubical compartment with no lid

KIT 1 — CONTENTS 5 PIECES — contents

KIT 2 — CONTENTS 16 PIECES — contents

16 pieces

builds — 4 cubical compartments in a 2×2 square array

CONTENTS ?? PIECES — CONVERSION KIT 1A — 1A

Kit 1A changes Kit 1 into Kit 2

1 How many pieces are there in: **a** Kit 1   **b** Kit 2   **c** Kit 1A?

2 Kit 3 builds a 3 × 3 square array of nine open cubical compartments. How many pieces are there in: **a** Kit 3   **b** Kit 2A (which changes Kit 2 to Kit 3)?

3 Investigate the number of pieces in Kits 4, 5, 6, 7 and in corresponding conversion Kits 3A, 4A, 5A, 6A.

4 Find a formula for the number of pieces in Kit nA.

The solar system

One of Kepler's laws of planetary motion is:
The square of the period (T) of a planet's revolution round the sun is directly proportional to the cube of its mean distance (D) from the sun.

1 For the earth, $T = 1$ (year) and $D \doteqdot 93$ (million miles). Show that $T^2 = \left(\dfrac{D}{93}\right)^3$.

2 Show that Mercury's 'year' (period of revolution) is about 0·24 of our year, or nearly 88 days.

3 Calculate the periods of revolution of some of the other planets shown in the Table.

Planet	Mean distance from sun, D (million miles)
Mercury	36
Venus	67
Mars	142
Jupiter	484
Saturn	887
Uranus	1782
Neptune	2792
Pluto	3700

4 a Use your results in question **3** to calculate the orbital velocities V of the planets you chose
in: (i) mph   (ii) miles per second.
   b Do planets nearer the sun move faster than ones further away?
   c Find a relationship (using the proportion symbol $\propto$) between V and D.
   d Planets move in elliptical orbits. Do you think they orbit at a steady speed? Give a reason
for your answer.

Athletics World Records

Here are tables of running and jumping records before the 1987 World Championship:

Event	100 m	200 m	400 m	800 m	1500 m
Men	9·93 s	19·72 s	43·86 s	1 min 41·73 s	3 min 29·46 s
Women	10·76 s	21·71 s	47·60 s	1 min 53·28 s	3 min 52·47 s

Event	5000 m (men) 3000 m (women)	10 000 m	Marathon	Hurdles 110 m/100 m	Hurdles 400 m
Men	12 min 58·39 s	27 min 7·81 s	2 h 7 m 12 s	12·93 s	47·02 s
Women	8 min 22·66 s	30 min 13·74 s	2 h 21 m 6 s	12·25 s	52·94 s

Event	High jump	Long jump	Triple jump	4 × 100 m relay	4 × 400 m relay
Men	2·42 metres	8·90 metres	17·97 metres	37·83 s	2 min 56·16 s
Women	2·08 metres	7·45 metres	—	41·37 s	3 min 15·92 s

1 In the 1987 World Championship, these new records were set:
   a Men's 100 m, 9·83 s   **b** Women's high jump, 2·09 m.
   Which showed the greater improvement over the previous record?

2 a Draw a graph of time against distance for the men's track events
from 100 m to 1500 m.
   b Explain the shape of the graph.
   c Estimate a record time for: (i) the 1000 m   (ii) the 2000 m.
   d Repeat **a**, **b** and **c** for the women's track events up to 1500 m.

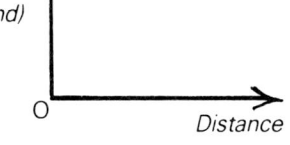

Time (to nearest second)

O   Distance

3 a Calculate the average speeds of men and women over the various distances in:
   (i) m/s   (ii) km/h.
   b Are the women's performances closer to the men's in short, medium or long distance
events?

4 Use the data in the table above question **1** to compare the men's and women's records in:
   a the high jump   **b** the long jump.

5 Use the data below for the high jump record (in metres) at 10-yearly intervals to:
a describe how the record has improved
b compare men's and women's performances.

Year	1905	1915	1925	1935	1945	1955	1965	1975	1985
Men	1·97	2·01	2·03	2·07	2·11	2·12	2·28	2·30	2·41
Women	1·37	1·47	1·62	1·65	1·71	1·73	1·91	1·95	2·07

6 Investigate: **a** Current Records—British and International.
b Improvements in particular events over the years.
c School Records.

The treasure hunt

At the 'Spy Glass Inn' Jim overhears the pirates discussing where they have buried their treasure.
'The Night Watch were at the crossroads. To avoid them, we left the road and cut across the moor for a mile before striking the other road. *Halfway* along this short-cut we buried the treasure . . .'
A brawl between two pirates means that Jim cannot hear the rest.

1 If the roads the pirates talk about intersect at right angles, investigate the complete set of possible positions of the treasure.

Draw two lines at right angles, and use a 5 cm strip of paper to represent the mile journey across the moor.

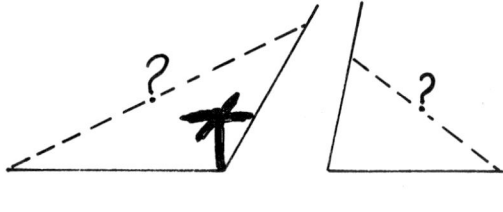

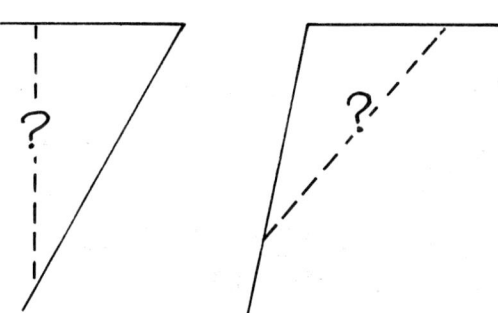

2 Suppose the pirates had said that the treasure was buried $\frac{3}{4}$ of the way along the short-cut . . . Investigate.

3 Suppose the roads had intersected at an angle of 45°, and the treasure was buried at the halfway point . . . Investigate.

$$F + \cfrac{R}{A + \cfrac{C}{T + \cfrac{I}{O + \cfrac{N}{S}}}}$$

Mathematicians have always been interested in patterns of fractions.

For example they have found that: $\sqrt{2} = 1 + \cfrac{1}{2 + \cfrac{1}{2 + \ldots}}$

1 a Check this for $1 + \cfrac{1}{2}$, $1 + \cfrac{1}{2 + \cfrac{1}{2}}$, $1 + \cfrac{1}{2 + \cfrac{1}{2 + \cfrac{1}{2}}}$, $1 + \cfrac{1}{2 + \cfrac{1}{2 + \cfrac{1}{2 + \cfrac{1}{2}}}}$.

b Compare the value of $\sqrt{2}$ by calculator

The sequence of fractions above can extend 'to infinity', but some common fractions can be expressed in a similar, but finite, form. For example,

$$\frac{5}{8} = \cfrac{1}{\frac{8}{5}} = \cfrac{1}{1 + \frac{3}{5}} = \cfrac{1}{1 + \cfrac{1}{\frac{5}{3}}} = \cfrac{1}{1 + \cfrac{1}{1 + \frac{2}{3}}} = \cfrac{1}{1 + \cfrac{1}{1 + \cfrac{1}{\frac{3}{2}}}} = \cfrac{1}{1 + \cfrac{1}{1 + \cfrac{1}{1 + \frac{1}{2}}}}$$

2 Check the result above 'backwards'.

3 Show that $\dfrac{5}{9} = \cfrac{1}{1 + \cfrac{1}{1 + \cfrac{1}{4}}}$

4 In the same kind of way, extend: **a** $\dfrac{4}{7}$ **b** $\dfrac{11}{21}$ **c** $\dfrac{13}{25}$

5 Investigate the form of fractions, like those above, which produce 1's in every place except the last one.

Regular hexagons

Jill is making regular hexagons with matchsticks arranged in equilateral triangles.

Number of matches in each side	Number of new matches	Total number of matches
1	12	12
2	...	...
...	...	...

1 Copy the headings, and fill in all the numbers.

2 Continue the investigation for hexagons with sides 4 and 5 matchsticks in length.

3 Find formulae for:
   a the number of new matchsticks
   b the total number of matchsticks, for a pattern with outer sides n matchsticks long.

4 How many boxes of matches (average contents 46) would be needed for a 10-matchstick side pattern?

ISBN Book Codes

Look inside the first page of this book, and you will see its International Standard Book Number (ISBN).

0	216	92946	6
Code English-speaking Nation	Blackie (Publisher)	This book	Check digit

Every book has a 10 digit code number like this.

The meaning of the check digit can be seen from this calculation for the ISBN for *Mathematics in Action*, **Book 2**, 0 216 91911 8.

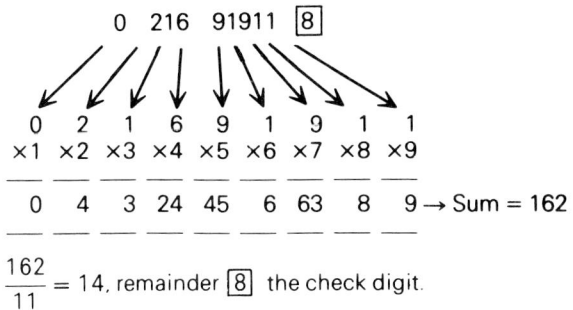

$$\frac{162}{11} = 14, \text{ remainder } \boxed{8} \text{ the check digit.}$$

1 Check the check digit for:
  a This book.   **b** The Chambers ISBN for this book (see inside first page).

2 There is another way of finding the check digit:
Multiply each of the 9 digits by 10, 9, 8, ..., 2 in order, and add the products. Again the check digit is related to multiples of 11. Can you find out how, by using the ISBN numbers above?

3 In the ISBN 0 205 08059 2, the check digit is correct, but two digits have become interchanged. Find out which ones.

4 Can you find the missing digit in 0 550 757 ● 2 8?

Measure for measure

Many methods and tools for measuring length have been devised to fit the needs of particular jobs.

 One example is the method of measuring the tiny gap in spark plugs. A set of metal strips of known thickness has been made, known as feeler gauges.

By using one or more gauges, you can measure many different sizes of gap.
For example, if you have 3 blades of thickness 2, 5 and 7 thou (thousandths of an inch), you can measure gaps of 2, 5, 7, 9, 12, 14 thou by using one, two or all three blades. Check this.

1 The blades in one set have thicknesses of 1, 2, 3, 4 and 5 thou. Find all the gap sizes that can be measured with this set.

In the land of Blink, where the people are called Blinkers, they do not use a ruler to measure length, but a curious set of rods of fixed lengths called Blinks. These rods can be used to measure a whole range of lengths by means of suitable additions and subtractions.
For example, with two rods of lengths 2 Blinks and 5 Blinks, you can have:

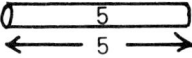
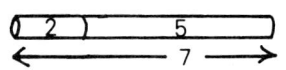
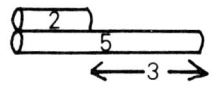

2 What lengths could be measured with rods 1, 2 and 5, blinks long?

3 The set used by the Blinkers contains five rods, which can be used to measure every length from 1 Blink to 121 Blinks. Investigate the lengths of the five rods.

Maximising volumes

Tough Tubes PLC make metal frames for containers.

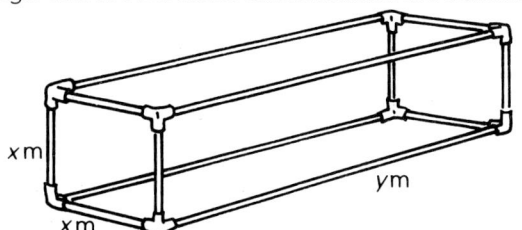 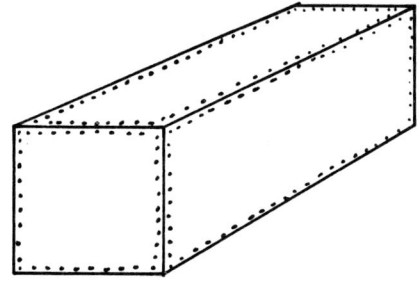

A customer wants a container in the form of a cuboid, with a square cross-section, which requires 60 m of tubing for the frame. Naturally the customer also wants the container to have the greatest possible volume. Tough Tubes Research Department has to calculate the dimensions of the container.

1 Write down an expression for the total length of tubing needed for the frame in terms of x and y.

2 Form an equation, and make y the subject.

3 Write down an expression for the volume of the container in terms of: **a** x and y　**b** x alone.

4 Copy and complete this table:

x (m)	0	1	2	3	4	5	6	7	8
Volume of box (Vm³)									

5 Draw a graph of V against x.

6 Which value of x gives the maximum value of V?

7 The customer has a change of plan and asks for a container which is a triangular prism with an equilateral triangle cross-section.

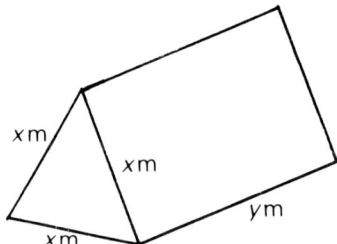

Investigate how to maximise the volume of this container, again using 60 m of tubing for the frame.

Tiling a roof

John tiles roofs. He uses tiles which are 1 foot long.
He overlaps each tile by $\frac{1}{3}$ of its length, like this:

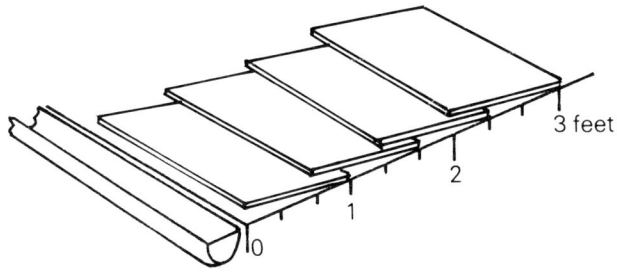

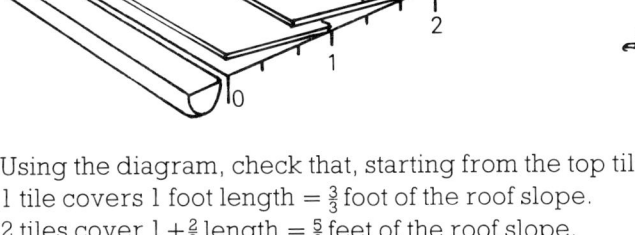

3 feet

Using the diagram, check that, starting from the top tile:
1 tile covers 1 foot length $= \frac{3}{3}$ foot of the roof slope.
2 tiles cover $1 + \frac{2}{3}$ length $= \frac{5}{3}$ feet of the roof slope.
3 tiles cover $\frac{5}{3} + \frac{2}{3}$ length $= \frac{7}{3}$ feet of the roof slope.

1 Copy and complete:

Number of tiles	1	2	3	4	5	6	n
Length covered (feet)	$\frac{3}{3}$	$\frac{5}{3}$	$\frac{7}{3}$				

n tiles cover L feet of slope. Write down the formula for L in terms of n. What length would be covered by 22 tiles?

2 John found that he had to calculate the number of tiles needed to cover the roof. Change your formula round to find n in terms of L. How many tiles would he need for lengths of:
a 15 feet   **b** 25 feet   **c** 40 feet?

3 Investigate the situation for tiles which have an overlap of:
a $\frac{2}{3}$ of a tile   **b** $\frac{1}{2}$ of a tile   **c** $\frac{3}{4}$ of a tile.
Can you find a formula for the number of tiles needed for a length L feet of roof, with an

overlap of $\dfrac{x}{y}$ of a tile, where $x < y$?

Bella's problem

1

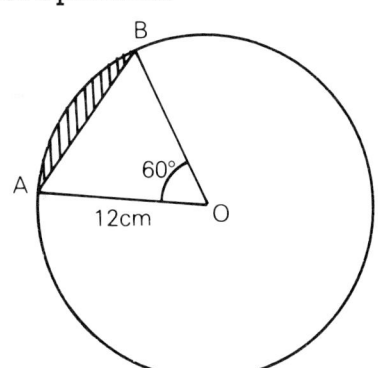

Calculate the area of:
a sector OAB
b triangle OAB
c the shaded segment

2

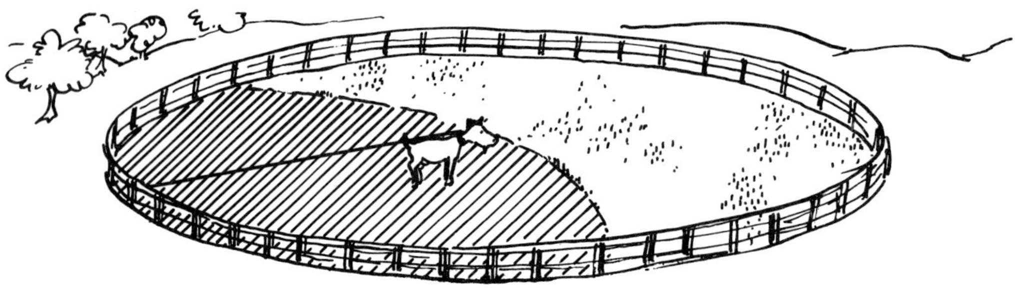

Bella can just reach the centre of her circular field if she pulls her tethering rope tight. The rope is 12 m long.

What percentage of the field can she graze?

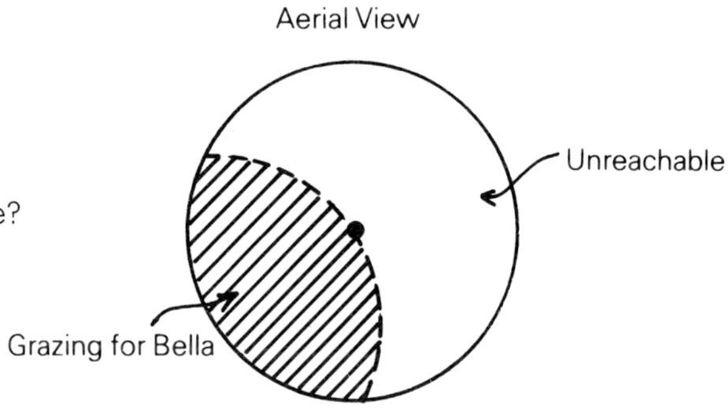

Aerial View

Unreachable

Grazing for Bella

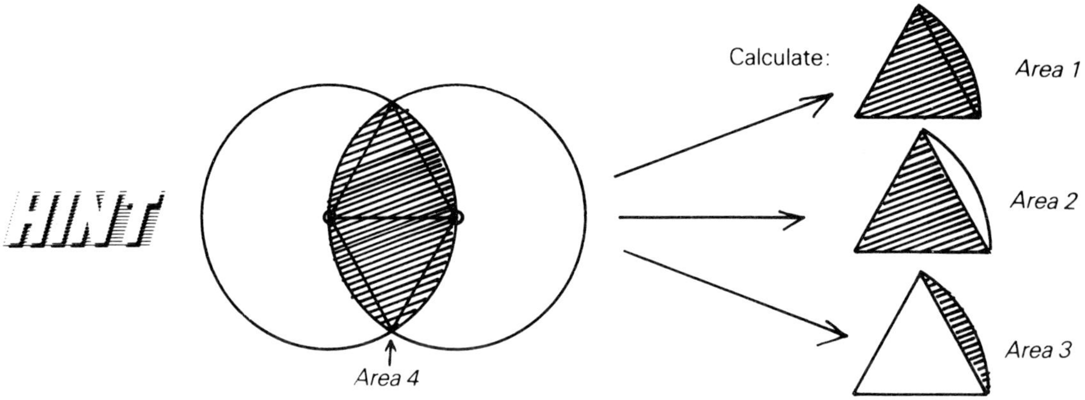

HINT

Calculate:

Area 1

Area 2

Area 3

Area 4

A Bypass

The A1031 trunk road ran right through Queuetown. After years of argument a bypass was started in May 1984 and completed in May 1988. Traffic surveys were carried out at the points shown in the sketch below.

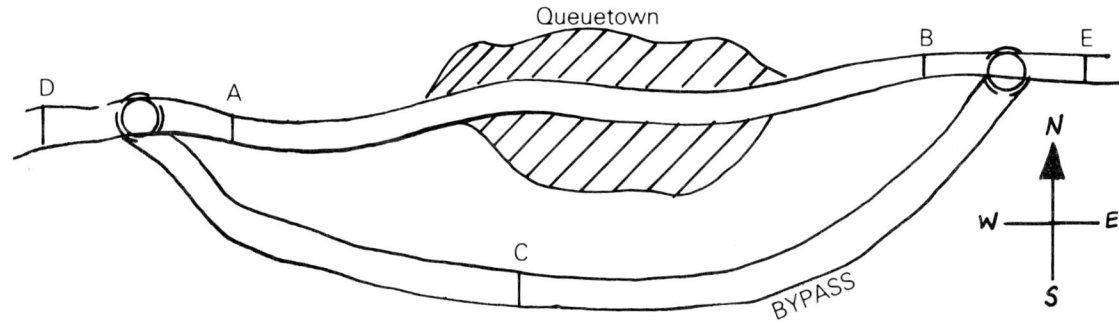

Queuetown

D   A   B   E

C

BYPASS

N
W — E
S

Starting hour	Number of vehicles, and direction of travel									
	1984				1988					
	A	A	B	B	A	A	B	B	C	C
	East	West	East	West	East	West	East	West	East	West
06 00	45	15	38	24	24	17	12	18	64	58
07 00	562	243	188	484	328	85	126	347	476	326
08 00	943	260	429	805	749	226	249	650	623	492
09 00	472	263	474	316	364	238	225	430	428	420
10 00	415	239	372	210	128	190	183	210	431	370
11 00	389	183	314	187	134	170	162	190	384	280
12 00	262	250	243	220	109	221	140	136	293	277
13 00	284	318	263	265	146	230	203	193	314	343
14 00	362	396	248	221	162	312	230	257	482	400
15 00	384	462	480	229	243	321	256	282	390	376
16 00	324	628	626	343	368	490	582	260	285	390
17 00	423	943	619	328	390	862	749	213	183	533
18 00	218	524	210	213	213	310	316	118	130	226
19 00	140	316	244	168	102	104	147	78	94	104
20 00	78	194	138	92	84	70	83	52	102	83

Imagine that you work in the Local Authority Roads Department, and have been asked for a Report on the effect of the new bypass on traffic through Queuetown. Analyse all the data and decide how to present the Report. Here are some suggestions that might help you.

For 1984

1 a Describe what happened between: (i) 7 and 9 am   (ii) 4 and 6 pm.
   b Calculate the net flow of traffic into Queuetown for each hour of the day.
   c Construct a cumulative frequency table, and draw a cumulative frequency curve, for the traffic at A flowing: (i) East   (ii) West.

For 1988

2 a Construct a table of the total traffic for each hour of the day at: (i) D   (ii) E.

b Calculate the total traffic passing through C from 6 am to 9 pm flowing: (i) East (ii) West.

c Overall, does more traffic flow East or West: (i) through Queuetown (ii) along the bypass?

Changes between 1984 and 1988

3 Use figures to support your answers to these questions:
  a Is Queuetown quieter or busier since the bypass was built?
  b Has the total traffic in the area increased?
  c Do you think that there was much through traffic before the bypass was built?
  d Has traffic which previously used other routes been attracted to use the bypass?

4 Queuetown depended on tourist trade and passing trade for a significant part of its income Has the bypass helped or hindered this? What other social considerations have to be taken into account?

A Camping Catalogue

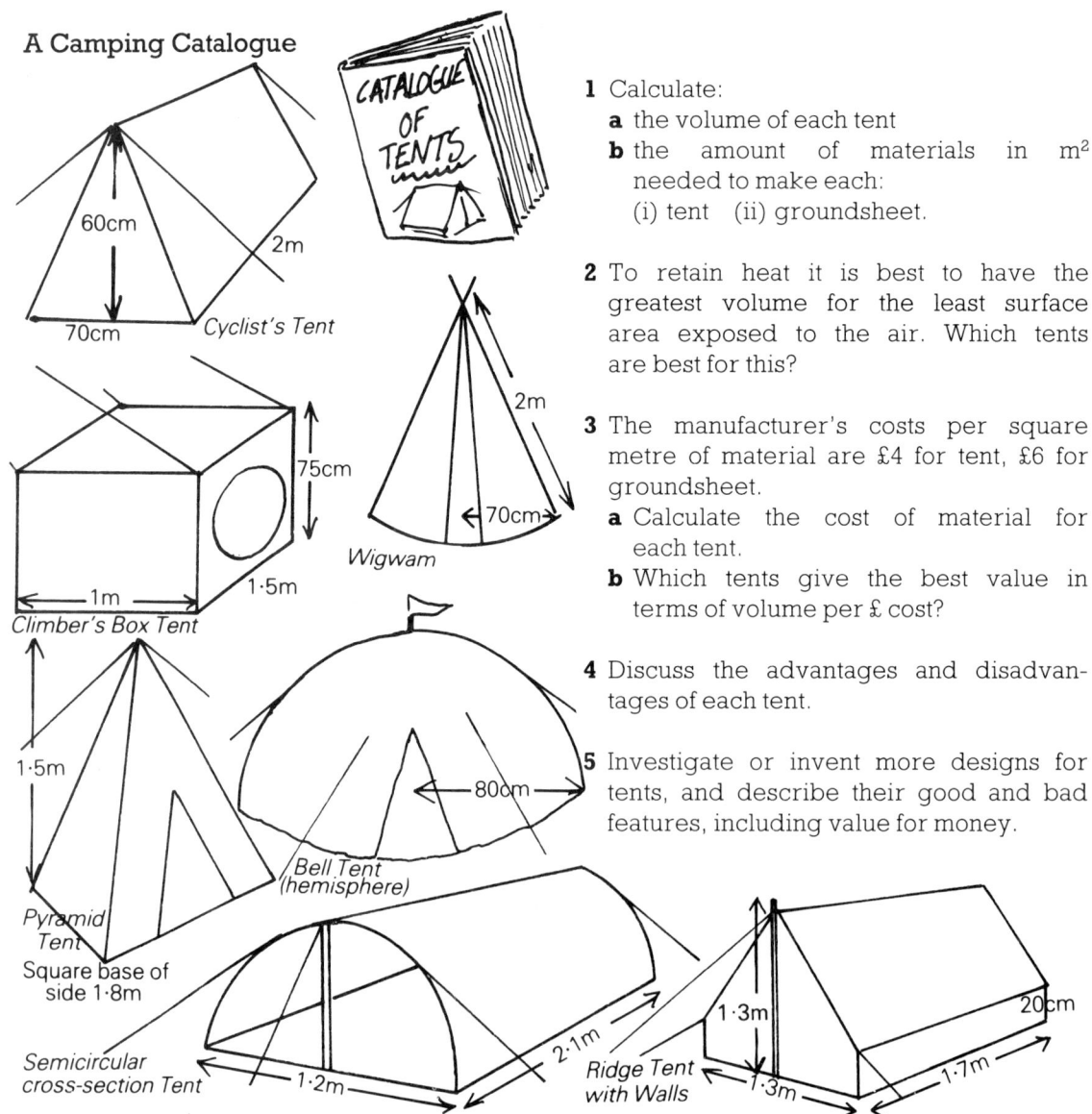

CATALOGUE OF TENTS

60cm / 2m / 70cm — *Cyclist's Tent*

75cm / ←70cm→ / 2m — *Wigwam*

1m / 1·5m — *Climber's Box Tent*

1·5m — *Pyramid Tent* — Square base of side 1·8m

Bell Tent (hemisphere) — ←80cm→

Semicircular cross-section Tent — 1·2m — 2·1m

Ridge Tent with Walls — 1·3m — 1·3m — 1·3m — 1·7m — 20cm

1 Calculate:
  a the volume of each tent
  b the amount of materials in m² needed to make each:
     (i) tent (ii) groundsheet.

2 To retain heat it is best to have the greatest volume for the least surface area exposed to the air. Which tents are best for this?

3 The manufacturer's costs per square metre of material are £4 for tent, £6 for groundsheet.
  a Calculate the cost of material for each tent.
  b Which tents give the best value in terms of volume per £ cost?

4 Discuss the advantages and disadvantages of each tent.

5 Investigate or invent more designs for tents, and describe their good and bad features, including value for money.

Repayment mortgages—how many years still to pay?

Each year Mr and Mrs Higgs receive a statement from their Building Society telling them how much they repaid in the previous year, and the amount still owing. Their loan is for £10 000.

ACCOUNT NUMBER B62342	YEAR ENDED 30 SEP 1988

Amount owing (£) 1 Oct 1987		10 000.00
Gross interest charged	1200.00	
Less tax relief	324.00	
Net interest charged	876.00	876.00
Total owing		10 876.00
Less repayments		1 440.00
Amount owing (£) 30 Sep 1988		9 436.00

1 a The gross interest is £1200. Calculate this interest as a percentage of the loan.
  b Income tax relief of £324 is allowed on the interest of £1200. Calculate this as a percentage of the interest.
  c How much did Mr and Mrs Higgs repay each month?

2 Assuming the same rates of interest, tax relief and repayments, repeat the Building Society calculations for the following year.

3 Draw a flowchart to calculate the amount owing each year.

4 Investigate the effect on the number of years needed to repay the loan of:
  a (i) an increase of 1%   (ii) a decrease of 1%, in the mortgage rate
  b paying back an extra £20 a month.

The wheel of fortune

This electronic Wheel of Fortune starts at O, and flashes a light every time the pointer, turning clockwise, passes a multiple of 10° (at 1, 2, 3, . . .), until it flashes at O again.

The second time round it flashes every 20° (at 2, 4, 6, . . .) until it flashes at O again; then every 30°, and so on.

1 Copy and complete the table, continuing it until you find a short way of calculating the number of flashes needed to return to O exactly.

Flash angle	10°	20°	30°	40°	50°
Number of flashes to return to O					
No. of times pointer passes O					

2 How many: **a** 200° flashes   **b** 300° flashes are needed to return to O?

Throwing light on cameras

The *f*-number on the aperture-control ring of a camera lens tells you about the size of the near-circular aperture, or opening, which allows light through to the film.

The standard *f*-number sequence is:

1·0, 1·4, 2·0, 2·8, 4·0, 5·6, 8, 11, 16, 22, 32, 45, 64.

Reducing the *f*-number by one setting, for example from 11 to 8, doubles the light allowed through the aperture (by doubling the area of the aperture). So the smaller the *f*-number, the larger the aperture.

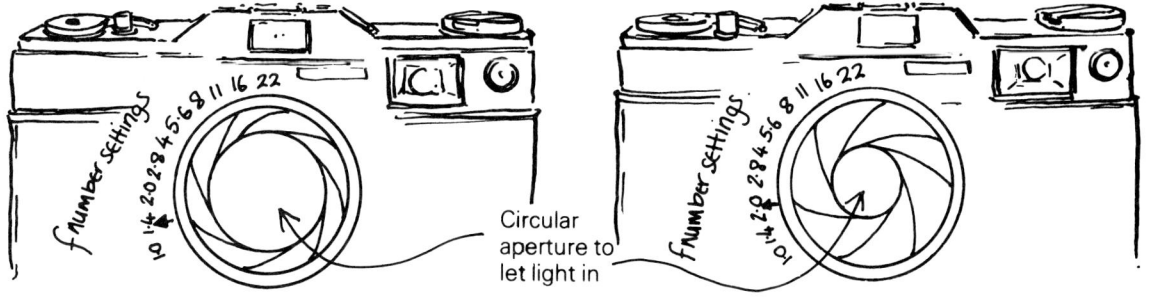

The setting on this camera is $f/1\cdot4$.   The setting on this camera is $f/2\cdot0$.

1 The aperture at $f/1\cdot4$ is a circle with radius $1\cdot6$ cm. Calculate:
   a the area of the aperture at: (i) $f/1\cdot4$ (ii) $f/2\cdot0$ (half the area at $f/1\cdot4$)
   b the radius of the aperture at $f/2\cdot0$.

2 Copy and complete this table:

Setting (s)	1·0	1·4	2·0	2·8	4·0		64
Area (cm²)	16·08	8·04					
Radius (r cm)	2·26	1·6					

3 Draw a graph of r against s, using the axes and scales shown.

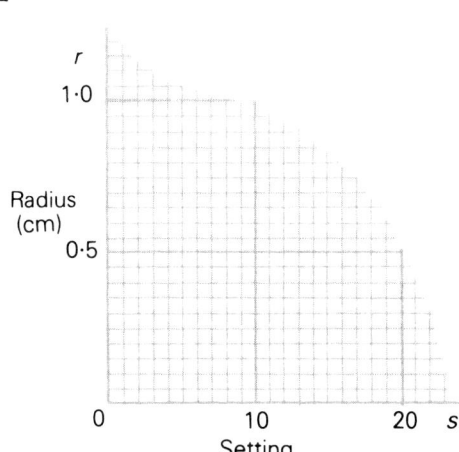

4 Find the equation connecting s and r.

5 Study the sequence of *f*-numbers: $1\cdot0$, $1\cdot4$, $2\cdot0$, $2\cdot8$, $4\cdot0$, ..., 64, which are correct to 2 significant figures. Write down: **a** the next two *f*-numbers
   b a formula for the *f* number following setting s.

Clothes poles

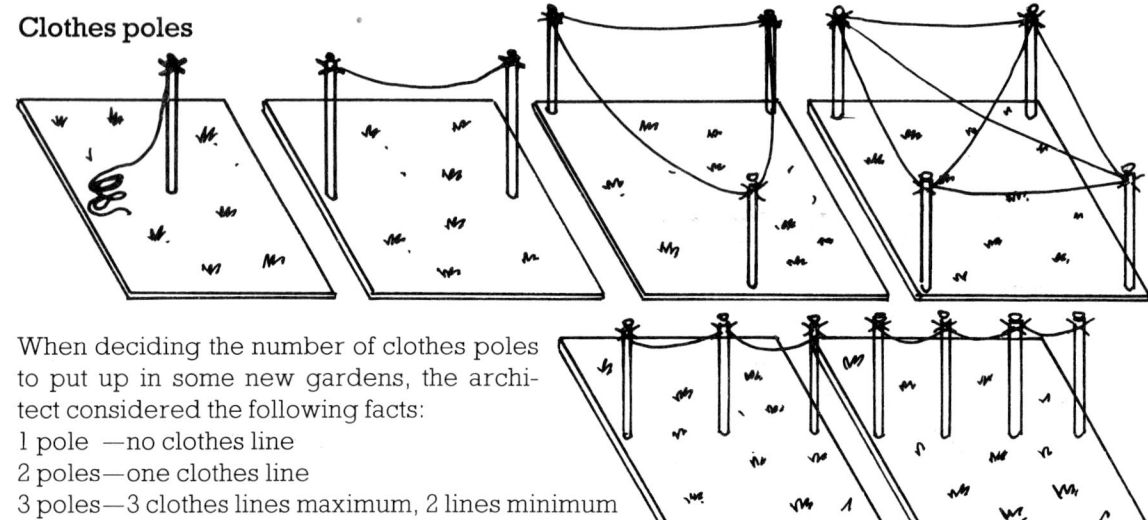

When deciding the number of clothes poles to put up in some new gardens, the architect considered the following facts:

1 pole —no clothes line
2 poles—one clothes line
3 poles—3 clothes lines maximum, 2 lines minimum
4 poles—6 clothes lines maximum, 3 lines minimum.

1 Find the maximum and minimum number for 5, 6, . . ., n poles.

2 Investigate the possible cases between the maximum and minimum numbers.

3 With lines over two or three poles (set in their 'maximum' positions), the rope can be strung without being hung between the same poles twice.
This is not possible in the case of four poles. Is it possible with 5, 6, . . ., n poles? Investigate.

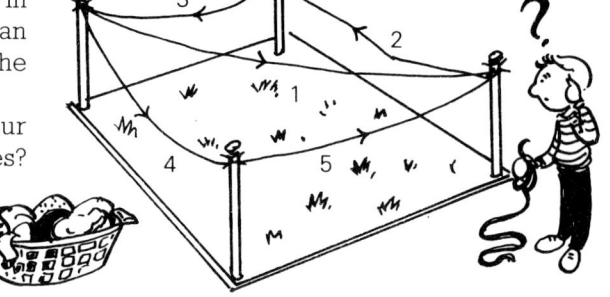

Wind chill

Wind makes the actual temperature appear to be lower than it is. This effect is called the *wind chill factor*,

$$W = (10\sqrt{v} + 10 - v)(33 - t),$$

where $t°$C is the actual temperature and v mph is the wind speed.

This table describes the various wind chill factors:

W	50	100	200	400	600	800	1000	1200	1400
Description	Hot	Warm	Pleasant	Cool	Very cool	Cold	Very cold	Bitterly cold	Flesh freezes

1 Calculate the wind chill factor, and describe the conditions, at these temperatures and wind speeds: **a** $-5°$C, 9 mph   **b** 20°C, 25 mph   **c** $-10°$C, 10 mph

2 Draw a graph of W against v for wind speeds from 0 to 50 mph in steps of 5 mph, at a temperature of 15°C.

3 Draw a graph of W against t for temperatures from -5°C to 25°C in steps of 5°, at a wind speed of 0 mph.

4 Contrast the effects on wind chill of: **a** change in temperature   **b** change in wind speed.

Car parking

Cars can park in various ways. For example:

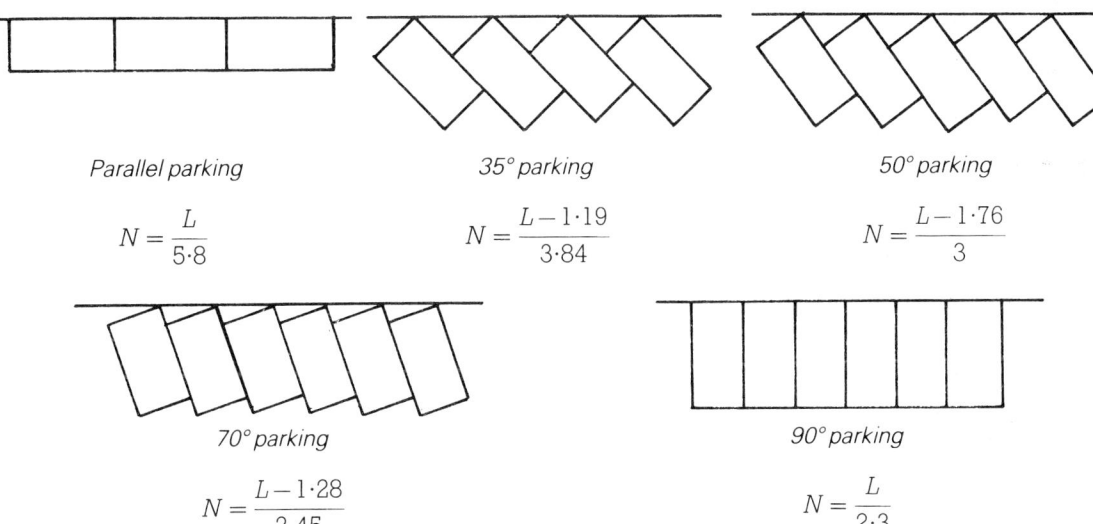

Parallel parking

$$N = \frac{L}{5 \cdot 8}$$

35° parking

$$N = \frac{L - 1 \cdot 19}{3 \cdot 84}$$

50° parking

$$N = \frac{L - 1 \cdot 76}{3}$$

70° parking

$$N = \frac{L - 1 \cdot 28}{2 \cdot 45}$$

90° parking

$$N = \frac{L}{2 \cdot 3}$$

These formulae give the number of spaces (N) that can be marked along L metres of pavement.

1 Compare the number of cars that can be parked along 100 m of pavement.

2 Draw a graph, and estimate the number for 60° and 45° parking.

3 A parking space is a rectangle 4·6 m by 2·2 m. Calculate:
   a how far each parking space projects into the road in **1**
   b which is the most efficient system. Can you see any other advantages or disadvantages in any of them?

2·2m

4·6m

4 In a car park, aisle widths are required as follows:

Type of parking	Aisle width
35°	3 m
50°	3·5 m
70°	5·5 m
90°	6·5 m

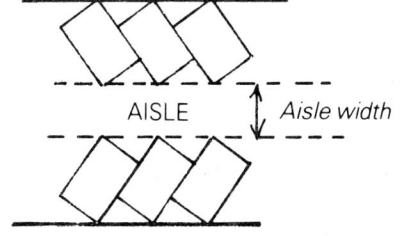

AISLE   Aisle width

Design a 50 m × 50 m car park. Use the formulae and other information to maximise the number of spaces available. Here are some ideas for a car park which is approximately 25 m square.

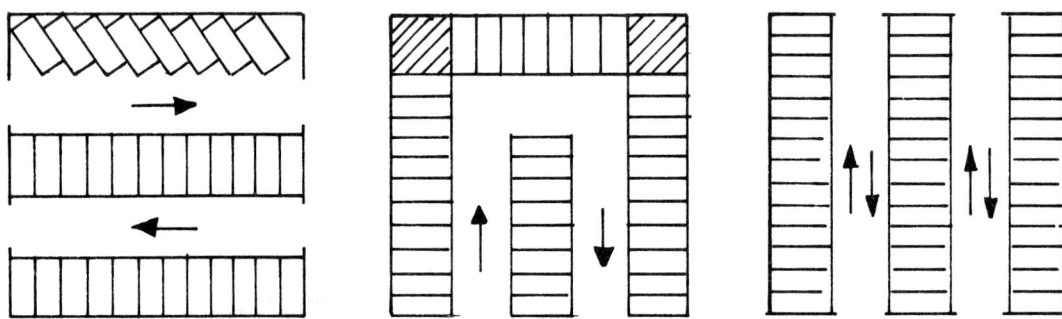

5 Investigate the school car park. Could you provide a better design?

Circles round triangles round circles round...

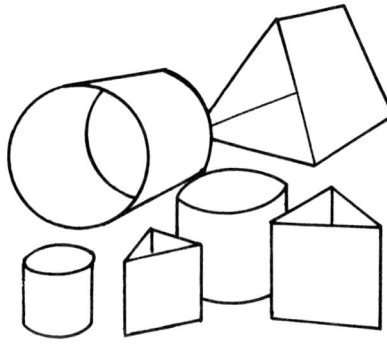

These children's toys stack inside each other, as you see on the right. Their cross-sections are circles and equilateral triangles. The corresponding sides of the triangles are parallel, and the radius of the smallest circle is 1 cm. The circles are numbered 1, 2, 3, 4.

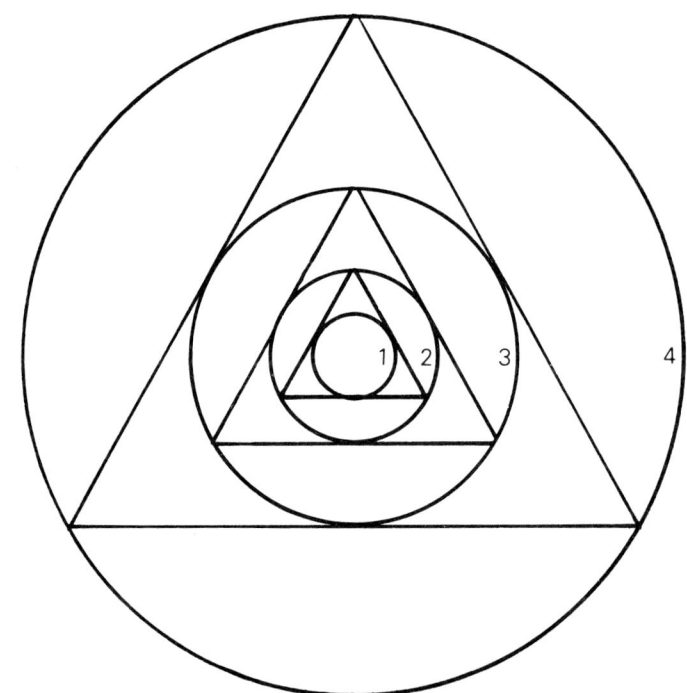

1 a Calculate the radius of circle: (i) 2 (ii) 3 (iii) 4.
  b Find a formula for the radius of the nth circle.

2 a Calculate the length of a side of each of the first three triangles.
  b Find a formula for the length of a side of the nth triangle.

3 Write down a formula for the area of: **a** the nth circle **b** the nth triangle.

5A's results at Riverside High School

Class 5A has a wide range of ability! Here are their exam results last year.

Pupil Number	Mathematics	Eng. Lang	Eng. Lit	French	German	History	Geography	Physics	Chemistry	Biology	Science	Computer Studies	Commerce	Art	C.D.T	Home Economics	Vehicle Tech	Metalwork	Music
1	A	A	B		C		B	C	B					C					
2	D	D	F			E	E			F	E								
3	E		E	D		D				F			E			E			
4	B	A	B	B		B	B			E						D			
5	A	A	C		C		C	B	C	C			C						
6	F	E	E			E				E				A	D		D	E	
7	A	A	A	B	C	A		C				C	D						
8	A	A	B	D		B	D					C		abs					
9	B	C	C			A		C	C			C					D	E	
10	B	B	D			D	B	C	U			B							
11	C	B	B			D				F			C		E	E			
12	E	E	E			E	E			E	E					C			
13	B	B	C	C	C		B		U			C							
14	B	A	A			A	B		U				B				B		
15		F	U										C		abs		D	F	
16	B	A	C	B		B				E		G							
17	D	C	F	D		D	E			F					D				
18	G	F	abs			abs											F	F	
19	D	C	U			abs				F			F			D			
20	F	E	G			E		G			D				F		F	F	
21	B	B	B	D			D			D			D			F			
22	C	D	B	E	C					F			D			E			
23	F	D	E			F							G		E		C		
24	D	C	F			D				D			D		D	C			
25	D	B	E	E		F				E			C						C
26	D	C	C	G		E				F			D	D					
27	D	C	C	D		E		D		F			D						
28	A	C	C	D	E		C	D				D							
29	A	A	A	C		A		C	C	C			C						
30	D	C	E	E		D				U			D			F			
31	C	E	F			E		E					E		E			D	
32	C	D	D			D		D							D			E	
33	C	C	B			C				E			D			D			
34	C	C	C			C	C	C	B										C
35	A	B	C		F		B	D		C		C							
36	D	D	G			G									G	G	C		
37	B	D	F			C		D				C	C						D
38	A	C	C		F		C	C	D					C					
39	D	F	G			E	D	D		D		G							
40	D	D	E			C				abs			E			C			

1 Produce a Report on the results for the Head teacher.

2 Design a method of comparing the results in different subjects, remembering that the overall ability of pupils taking different subjects will vary.

3 Perhaps you can analyse some statistics for your own school, or some National Statistics.

Areas and volumes

From the information given about each solid:
a write down a formula for its volume in terms of x and y
b find an expression for the ratio $x:y$ in each case.

1 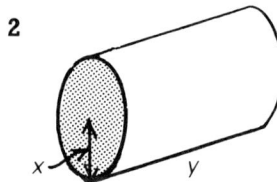 The sum of the areas of the two square ends is equal to the sum of the areas of the other four faces of the *cuboid*.
Hint. $V = x^2y$; $2x^2 = 4xy$, etc

2 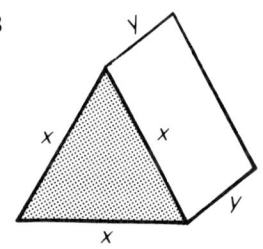 The sum of the areas of the ends is equal to the curved surface area of the *cylinder*.

3 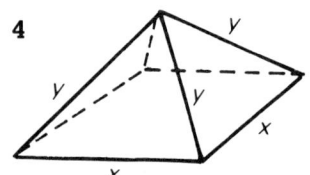 The sum of the areas of the ends is equal to the sum of the areas of the other three faces of the *prism*.

4 Twice the area of the square base is equal to the sum of the areas of the other four faces of the *pyramid*.

Communications around the world

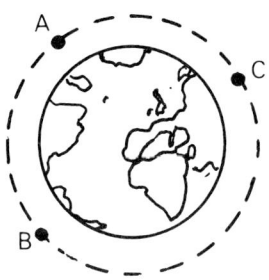

Deepspace International plan to place three communication satellites in the same orbit around the earth (radius R km). The satellites must be able to communicate directly with each other and must cover the whole circumference of the earth between them.

1 Make a sketch to show how they should be placed, and check by calculation that the lowest possible orbit is R km above the surface of the earth.

2 Repeat the problem in the case of 4, 5 and 6 satellites.

3 Find a formula for the angle at the centre of the earth to neighbouring satellites for n satellites.

4 The cost of putting a satellite in orbit varies directly as the height of the satellite. Investigate whether it is cheaper to have a small number or a large number of satellites in orbit.

Rockets and cones

Maria is a space fanatic. She is making model rockets, and finds that she needs lots of cones.
She starts by cutting out a 60° sector from a circle which has a radius of 10 cm, and making it into her first cone.

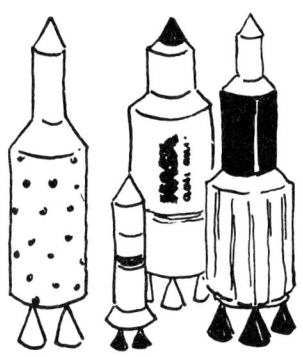

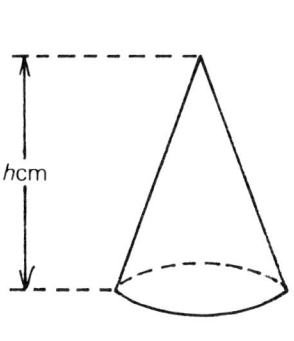

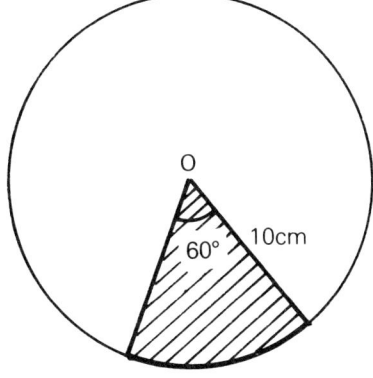

1 Calculate:
    a the circumference of the base of the cone
    b the radius of the base of the cone
    c the perpendicular height of the cone.

2 Repeat **1** when she cuts out sectors with angles of 120°, 180°, 240° and 300°.
Copy and complete this table:

Sector angle ($x°$)	60°	120°	180°	240°	300°
Height of cone (h cm)	9·9				

3 Draw a graph of h against x.

4 Show that the formula connecting h and x is $h^2 = 100 - \left(\dfrac{x}{36}\right)^2$.

Triblockbusters

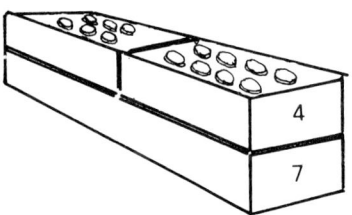

These 3 bricks make a tri-block since 4 sections + 3 sections = 7 sections.

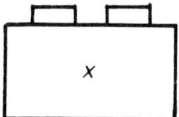

End view of
brick with
x sections

Example
Is it possible to make triblocks from these 3 bricks?

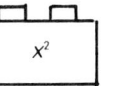 x^2 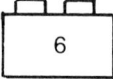 6 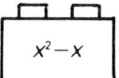 $x^2 - x$

(i) *Base $x^2 - x$*

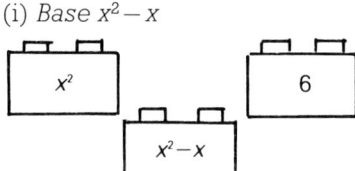

(ii) *Base x^2*

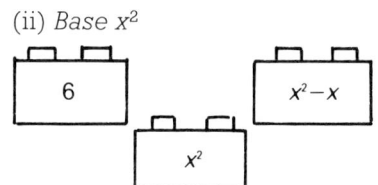

(iii) *Base 6*

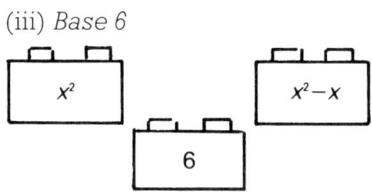

(i) $x^2 + 6 = x^2 - x$

$x = -6$
(not possible)

(ii) $6 + x^2 - x = x^2$

$x = 6$

(iii) $x^2 + x^2 - x = 6$
$2x^2 - x - 6 = 0$
$(2x + 3)(x - 2) = 0$
$x = -1\frac{1}{2}$ (not possible) or 2

Using these solutions, the lengths of the bricks, in sections, are:

(ii) 6, 30, 36   (iii) 4, 2, 6

Investigate whether triblocks can be made from these sets of bricks. Remember to find the lengths of all possible bricks.

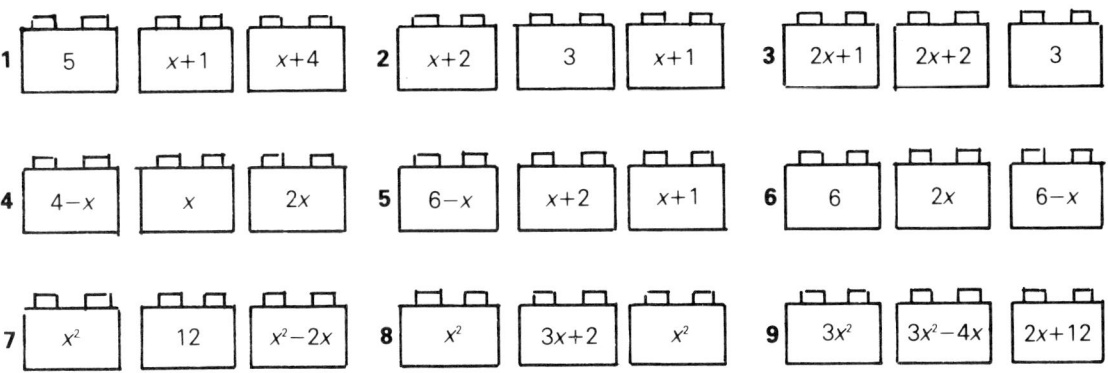

1 5 ⬚ $x+1$ ⬚ $x+4$ **2** $x+2$ ⬚ 3 ⬚ $x+1$ **3** $2x+1$ ⬚ $2x+2$ ⬚ 3

4 $4-x$ ⬚ x ⬚ $2x$ **5** $6-x$ ⬚ $x+2$ ⬚ $x+1$ **6** 6 ⬚ $2x$ ⬚ $6-x$

7 x^2 ⬚ 12 ⬚ x^2-2x **8** x^2 ⬚ $3x+2$ ⬚ x^2 **9** $3x^2$ ⬚ $3x^2-4x$ ⬚ $2x+12$

Domino dots

Ray and Keith make sets of dominoes. Ray makes the wooden shapes and Keith etches the dots on the dominoes.

1 Copy and complete this table up to a set with a double 6:

Highest double	0	1	2	3
Number of dominoes in set	1	3	6	

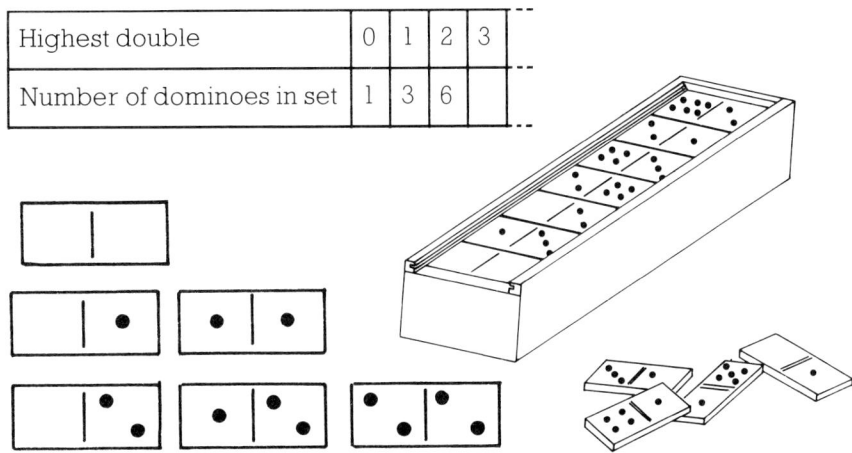

2 How many dominoes are in a set with a double: (i) 10   (ii) n?

Keith is more interested in the number of dots he has to etch in order to work out the cost.

3 Copy the sketch of the dominoes above, and extend it to double 3 and double 4 sets. Then copy and complete this table, and extend it as far as double 6:

Highest double		0	1	2	3
Extra number of dots to etch		0	3	9	18
Total number of dots to etch		0	3	12	30

Chess ladders

The Chess Club at Parkside High School run a chess ladder.

Each player can challenge the one immediately above.

A win means moving up a place, and a defeat means moving down a place.

Investigate the least number of games that must be played for positions on the ladder to be completely reversed (second bottom to second top, etc) when the number of pupils on the ladder is: **a** 2   **b** 3   **c** 4   **d** 5.

Continue the investigation for larger numbers. Find a rule for the least number of matches needed to reverse the order.

A round table

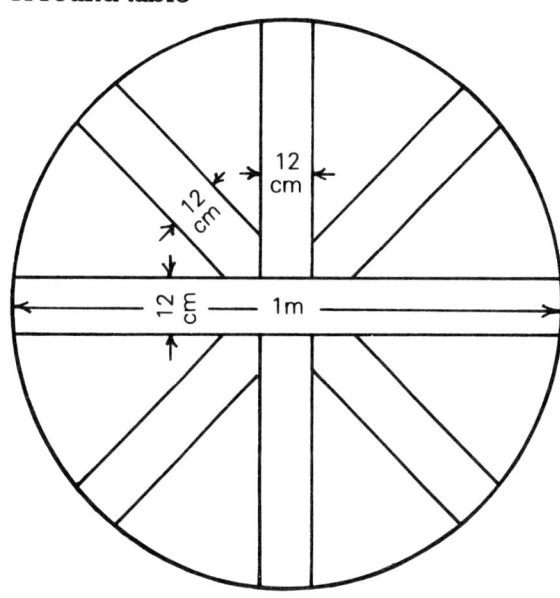

The diagram shows the design for a round table, to be made from 15 parts.

1 Make a scale drawing of the design, $\frac{1}{10}$th the actual size.

2 A carpenter is going to make this table. Write out detailed instructions on how to draw the outline of each part.

Football league competition

Class 5Z organise a competition in which each pupil taking part has to predict at the beginning of the season what the final position of each football team in the First Division will be at the end of the season.

At the end of the season, the pupil with fewest penalty points will be the winner. If you predict that a team will finish fourth in the league, and they finish ninth, you will have $9 - 4 = 5$ penalty points.

Similarly if they finish second, you will have $4 - 2 = 2$ penalty points.

A completely correct forecast would score 0 penalty points.

1 a Copy and complete this table for very small leagues:

Number of teams	2	3	4	5	6	7	8
Maximum penalty points							

b Calculate the maximum penalty points for a league with:
(i) 20 teams   (ii) 21 teams.
c Find a formula for the maximum number of penalty points for a league with n teams, when:
(i) n is even   (ii) n is odd.

2 Choose a league, ask friends to predict the final positions of the teams, and make a weekly progress check.

3 Draw a flowchart and write a computer program for calculating the penalty points.

4 Experiment with random forecasts, and compare these with predictions according to form.

Rolling polygons

An equilateral triangle

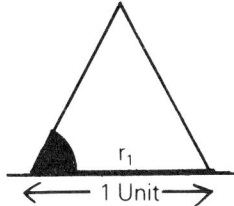

An equilateral triangle of side 1 unit is 'rolled' along the ground. How far does each vertex travel through the air from leaving the ground to arriving back on the ground again?

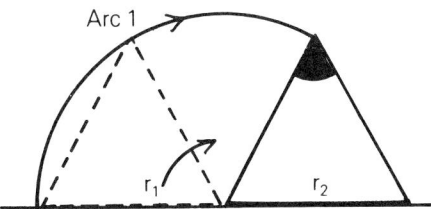

Follow the marked angle and its vertex.
What fraction of a complete circle is arc 1?
What is the radius of the circle?

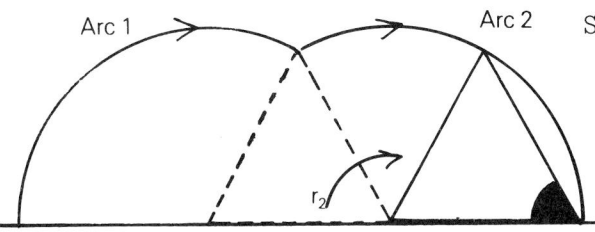

So what length is arc 1? (Keep π.) And arc 2?

Do you find that the total length is $\dfrac{4\pi}{3}$ units?

A square

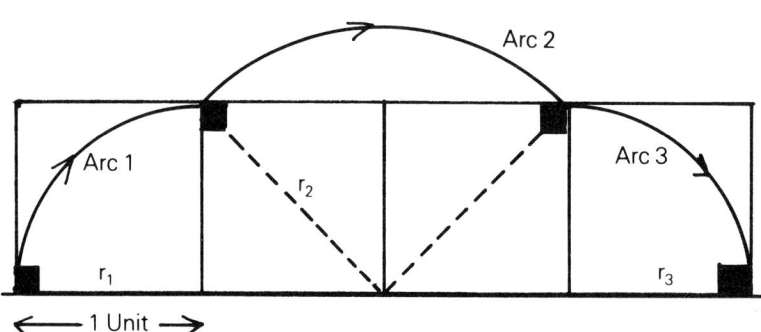

Remember—you are following one vertex, the one marked.

If you find the rolling square difficult to visualise cut out a square and turn it around as shown.

Use Pythagoras' Theorem to calculate r_2.

Show that arc $1 +$ arc $2 +$ arc $3 = \dfrac{\pi}{2}(2 + \sqrt{2})$ units.

A regular hexagon

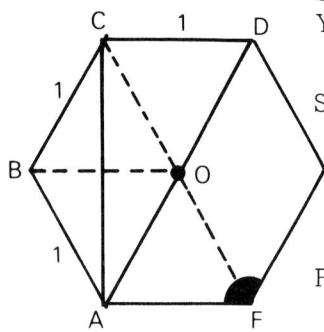

Show that AD $= 2$, and AC $= \sqrt{3}$.

You will have 5 arcs in rolling the hexagon right around.

Show that two of them have length $\dfrac{\pi}{3}$ units, two have length $\dfrac{\sqrt{3}\pi}{3}$ units, and one has length $\dfrac{2\pi}{3}$ units.

Find an expression with surds and π for the total length.

1 Find all possible postages under £1 which can be paid for with 13p and 18p stamps.

2

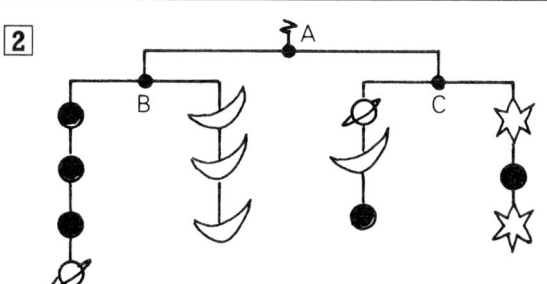

The mobile is pivoted at A, B and C. The sun shape ● weighs 2 g. Find the weight of each of the other shapes if the mobile remains balanced.

3 A wooden cube has its six faces painted red. It is then cut into eight identical cubes. How many red faces has each of these cubes? Investigate the same problem if the original cube is cut into twenty-seven smaller cubes.

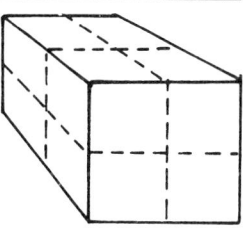

4 Can you find a quick way to calculate each sum of numbers?

a 6
b $1 + 2 + 3 + 4 + \cdots + 99 + 100$
7
c $8 + 4 + 2 + 1 + \frac{1}{2} + \frac{1}{4} + \frac{1}{8} + \cdots$
7
2
Hint Copy this square, and fill in all the areas:
3
5
1
2
9
8
6
4
5
1
5
9
7
3
2
8

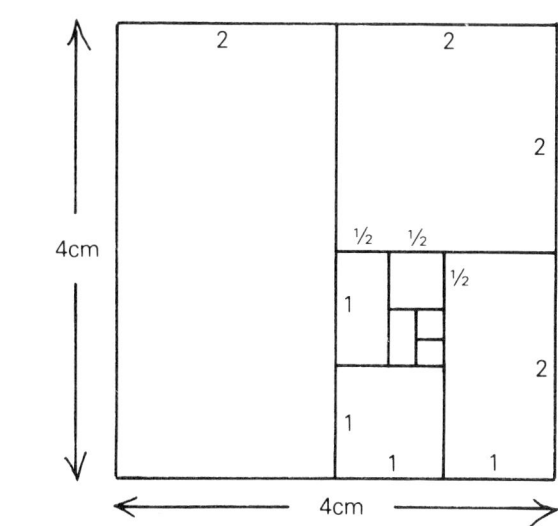

5 Jack is down by the river. He has two jugs; one holds 2 pints and the other holds 7 pints. How can he use them to measure 1, 2, 3, 4, 5, 6, 7, 8 or 9 pints exactly?

a Jill worked out the answer; her working is shown. Investigate.

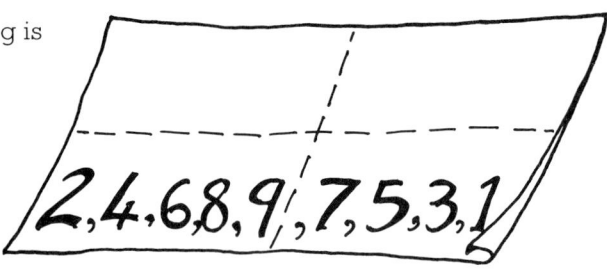

b If Jack had taken these two jugs to the river, what possible volumes of water might he have taken back to the camp site (assuming that he went back with a carefully measured amount)?

c Which pair of jugs shown here is the more versatile?

---

6 A company which manufactures drawing instruments plans to produce a ruler on which protractor markings are inscribed every 10°.
The ruler is to be 30 cm long by 3 cm wide.
The markings will be drawn from the midpoint of one edge of the ruler to another edge, as shown in this rough sketch.

Calculate the distances along the edges of the ruler to the points where the lines meet the edges.

7

(In **a** and **b**, simplify each term first.)

a $1-\dfrac{1}{2},\quad \left(1-\dfrac{1}{2}\right)\left(1-\dfrac{1}{3}\right),\quad \left(1-\dfrac{1}{2}\right)\left(1-\dfrac{1}{3}\right)\left(1-\dfrac{1}{4}\right),\ldots$

b $\dfrac{1}{1\times 2},\quad \dfrac{1}{1\times 2}+\dfrac{1}{2\times 3},\quad \dfrac{1}{1\times 2}+\dfrac{1}{2\times 3}+\dfrac{1}{3\times 4},\ldots$

c $\dfrac{2}{1+2},\quad \dfrac{3}{1+2+3},\quad \dfrac{4}{1+2+3+4},\ldots$

d $\dfrac{1}{1+2},\quad \dfrac{1+2}{1+2+3},\quad \dfrac{1+2+3}{1+2+3+4},\ldots$

8

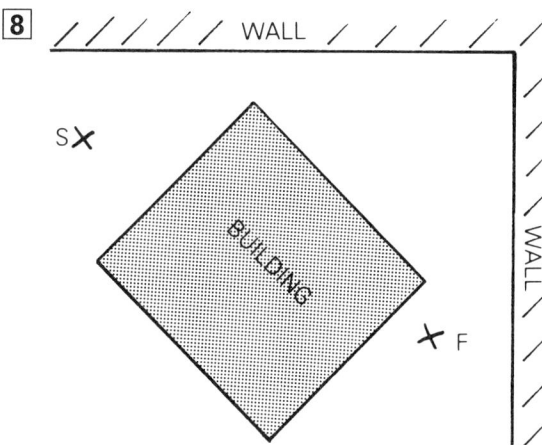

John has to run from S to F, touching both boundary walls as he goes.

Make a tracing, and construct the shortest route.

---

9 Three examples of consecutive numbers are shown on the number line.

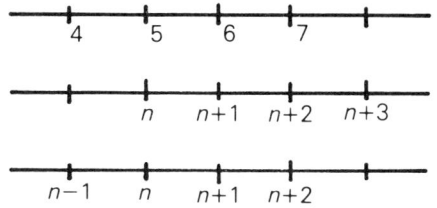

If a, b, c, d are consecutive numbers, prove that:

(i) $bc-ad = 2$ (ii) $bd-ac$ is always odd

(iii) $a+b+c+d$ is always even, but is never a multiple of 4

(iv) $a^2+d^2 = b^2+c^2+4$.

10 The fraction $\frac{1}{7} = 0.142857142857142857\ldots$ Your calculator cannot produce all these numbers.

Your calculator probably gives | 0.1428571 |, and the repeating pattern is not obvious.

But...

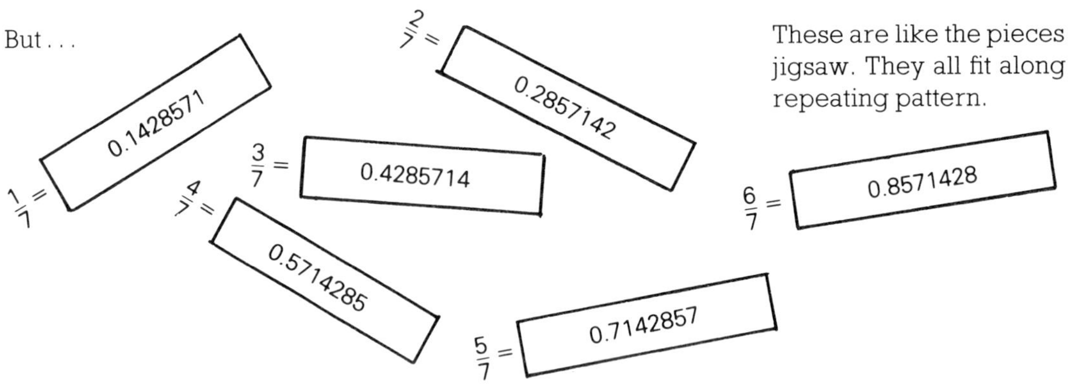

$\frac{1}{7} =$ 0.1428571

$\frac{2}{7} =$ 0.2857142

$\frac{3}{7} =$ 0.4285714

$\frac{4}{7} =$ 0.5714285

$\frac{5}{7} =$ 0.7142857

$\frac{6}{7} =$ 0.8571428

These are like the pieces of a jigsaw. They all fit along the repeating pattern.

... rearranging ...

shows the pattern.

0.1428571

0.2857142

0.4285714

0.5714285

0.7142857

0.8571428

OR

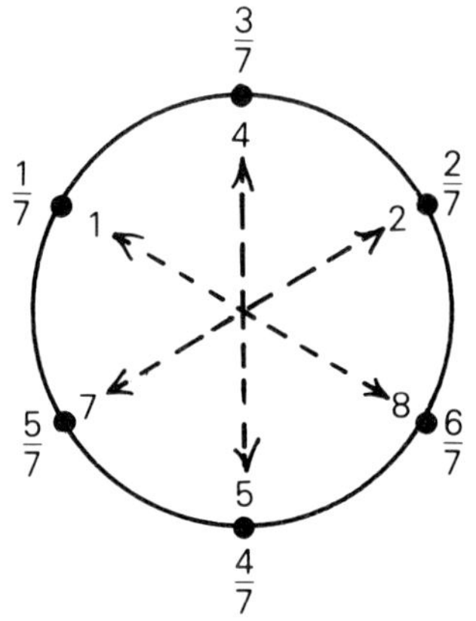

$\frac{3}{7}$ 4

$\frac{1}{7}$ 1 $\frac{2}{7}$

$\frac{5}{7}$ 7   8 $\frac{6}{7}$

$\frac{4}{7}$ 5

a Here are some pieces of another 'jigsaw'.

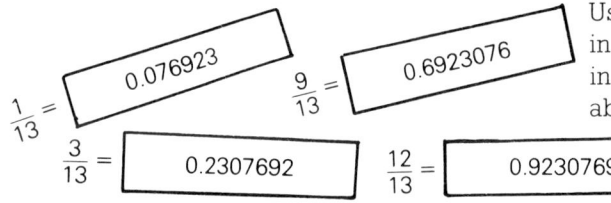

$\frac{1}{13} =$ 0.076923

$\frac{9}{13} =$ 0.6923076

$\frac{3}{13} =$ 0.2307692

$\frac{12}{13} =$ 0.9230769

Use these pieces to find the repeating pattern in the decimal expansion of $\frac{1}{13}$. Arrange this in two number circles, by studying the one above.

b Investigate the repeating pattern in the decimal expansion of:

(i) $\frac{1}{17}$ (ii) $\frac{1}{19}$ (You will have to discover the 'jigsaw pieces' using your calculator).

11 **a**   (i) Calculate $2^1, 2^2, 2^3, 2^4, 2^5, \ldots$

(ii) Is there a pattern in the last digit of each number? Show it in a number circle.

(iii) What will be the last digit of 2^{100}?

b   (i) Repeat your investigation for $3^n, 4^n, 5^n$, where $n = 1, 2, 3, \ldots$

(ii) In each case predict the last digit in the number raised to the power 100.

12 $l = 4(2m+1)$, $b = 4m^2 + 4m - 3$ and $h = 4m^2 + 4m + 5$.
a Compare the values of $l^2 + b^2$ with h^2 when $m = 1, 2, 3$.
b Prove that $l^2 + b^2 = h^2$.

---

13 Sheena is counting the number of people at a disco. When she counts in threes, there are 2 left over. When she counts in fives, there are 3 left over. When she counts in eights, there are 4 left over. How many were at the disco?

Is there only one possible answer?

---

14 **a** Can you find the smallest positive integer that can be made from the sum of two different pairs of squares?
b 1729 is the smallest positive integer that can be expressed as the sum of two different pairs of cubes. Find the two pairs.

15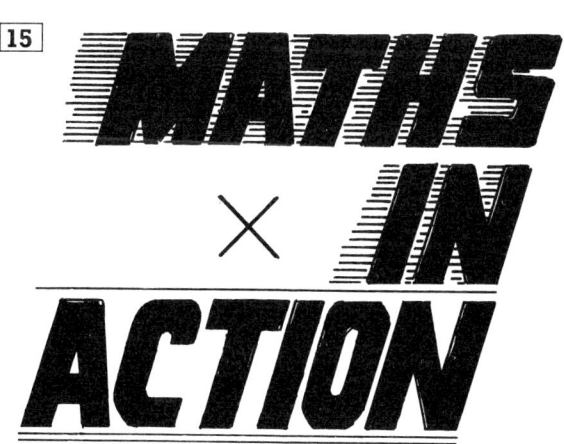

Mary was doing long multiplications by 20.

$$\begin{array}{r} 15\,341 \\ \times\,20 \\ \hline 306\,820 \\ \hline \end{array}$$

But she could not manage the one on the left. Each letter represents a different digit. Find a $\times\,20$ multiplication which fits it, and explain how you worked it out.

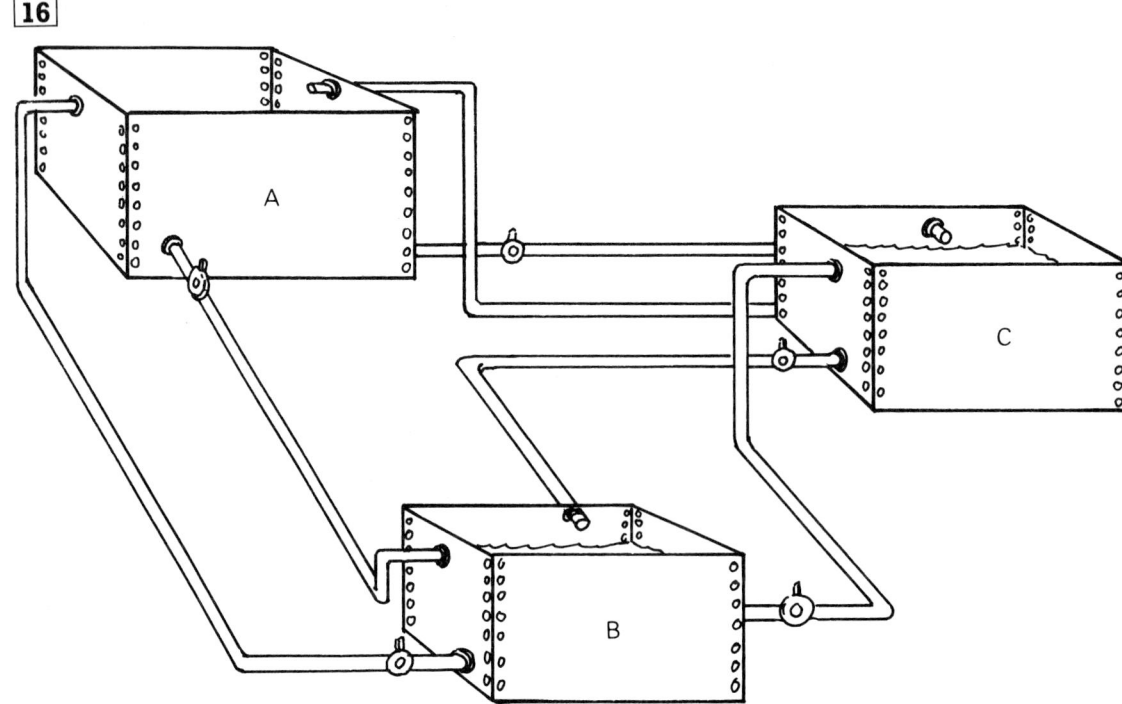

The valves in a system of water tanks are computer-controlled.
In an attempt to distribute the water equally among the three tanks the computer controls the pumping of water from the fullest tank to the others at certain intervals.

It is programmed to *double* the volume in the other two tanks.

For example:

Tank	A	B	C
Volume at start (gallons)	6	2	3
Volume after 1 cycle	1	4	6
Volume after 2 cycles	2	8	1
Volume after 3 cycles	4	5	2

a A fourth cycle is not possible. Why not?
When this happens, the computer considers that its job is done.

b How many cycles are possible if the number of gallons in the tanks is:
(i) 8, 3, 1   (ii) 7, 4, 2   (iii) 10, 2, 1?

c Investigate the starting volumes so that at least one cycle will occur.

d On one occasion, after 3 cycles, each tank contained 8 gallons. Investigate the possible starting volumes of water in the tanks.

Page 10 **Russian Multiplication**

1 a (8×9) **b** (12×15) **c** 7×25
  (4×18) (6×30) 3×50
  (2×36) 3×60 1×100
  1×72 1×120
  $8 \times 9 = 72$ $12 \times 15 = 180$ $7 \times 25 = 175$

  d 51×11
   25×22
   (12×44)
   (6×88)
   3×176
   1×352
   $51 \times 11 = 561$

3

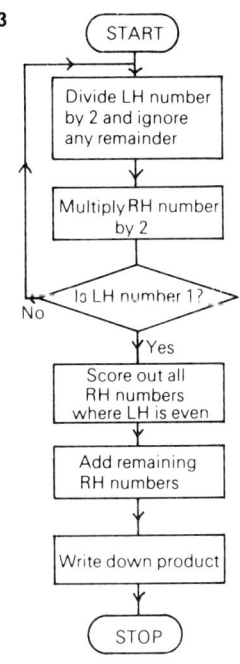

Page 10 **Hidden Words**

a

```
E C N E R E F M U C R I C
S S A R C O N D R A A T R
S E C T O R R T E O D A A
O G C N E O A R T S I N T
M M D E H G A H E G U G E
G E L C R I C I M E S C O
R N M A T H S P A R T E N
A T A N G E N T I I I N T
D A C T I O N A D D R O C
```

b

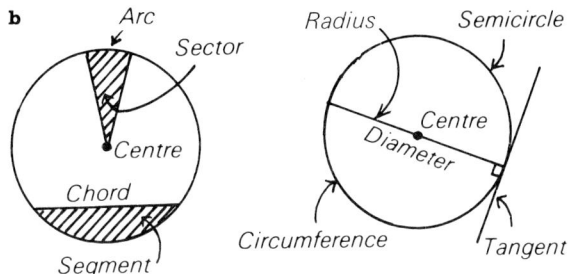

c Yes, in the last 3 rows.

Page 11 **Addition Table Squares**

1 a Same sum **b**

x	$x+1$
$x+1$	$x+2$

$x + (x+2) = (x+1) + (x+1)$

2 a Difference of 1 **b**

x	$x+1$
$x+1$	$x+2$

$(x+1)^2 = x(x+2) + 1$

3 Diagonal from top left to bottom right

Page 12 **Painted faces**

2 layers 16,   3 layers 33,   4 layers 56.

1	2	3	4	5	6	n
5	16	33	56	85	120	
1×5	2×8	3×11	4×14	5×17	6×20	$n(3n+2)$

Page 12 **Gift Cards**

a

Total Value £	Fiona 1	Fiona 2	Fiona 3	Eve 1	Eve 2	Eve 5	Colin 1	Colin 3	Colin 6
1	✓			✓			✓		
2		✓			✓		✓✓		
3			✓	✓	✓			✓	
4	✓		✓	✓✓			✓	✓	
5		✓	✓			✓	✓✓	✓	
6		✓✓		✓		✓			✓
7	✓	✓✓			✓	✓	✓		✓
8		✓	✓✓	✓	✓	✓	✓✓		✓
9			✓✓✓		✓✓	✓		✓	✓
10					✓✓	✓	✓	✓	✓
11				✓		✓✓			
12				✓	✓✓				✓✓

b Fiona £9, Eve £12, Colin £10 **c** Eve's best; Fiona's worst

Page 13   *Armchair puzzles*

Possible final positions are shown.

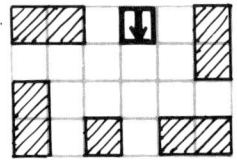

Page 14   *Bus Route Numbers*

1 a 00 to 99, 100 routes **b** (i) 260 (ii) 520
2 a 1000 **b** 17 576 **c** Letter followed by 2 numbers, 2600 ways; 2 numbers and a letter in any position, 7800 ways; 2 letters followed by 1 number, 6760 ways: 2 letters and 1 number in any position, 20 280 ways: 3 letters, 17 576 ways

Page 15   *Swimming*

1 a

Stroke	Back	Breast	Butterfly	Freestyle
Men	55 s	62 s	53 s	49 s
Women	61 s	68 s	58 s	55 s

b

Men	1·8 m/s	1·6 m/s	1·9 m/s	2·1 m/s
Women	1·7 m/s	1·5 m/s	1·7 m/s	1·8 m/s

c In decreasing speed order: Freestyle, Butterfly, Back, Breast
d (i) Butterfly (ii) Breast
2 Distance (m)   50   100   200   400
  a Time   22 s   49 s   1 min 47 s   3 min 48 s
  c Speed m/s   2·2   2·1   1·9   1·8
d As the distance increases the speed decreases

Page 15   *Design symmetry*

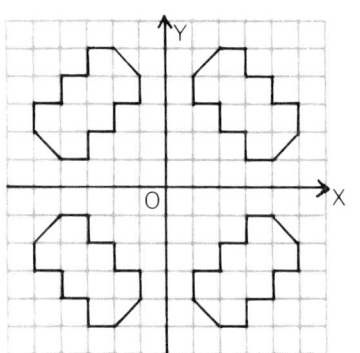

Page 16   *A day trip*

1 W.A., S.E., W.R., C.T.

2 a

Choice Order	1	2	3	4	5
Seaside	11	1	1	3	10
London	7	7	0	5	7
Zoo	0	12	6	1	7
Concert	8	0	9	7	2
Funfair	0	6	10	10	0

b (i) Seaside (ii) Seaside
4 Seaside 78, London 80, Zoo 75, Concert 83, Funfair 74. Concert would be chosen
6 a (i) Not possible (ii) Yes **b** London and Zoo
London: W.A., R.B., S.E., I.H., J.M., P.M., S.N., A.P., J.R., W.R., N.S., C.T., G.T., T.Y.
Zoo: J.A., T.C., J.F., T.F., R.M., T.R., K.S., S.T., A.W., K.W., P.Y., R.Y.

Page 18   *Equal shares*

2 3 × 3 cannot be divided into 2 equal parts

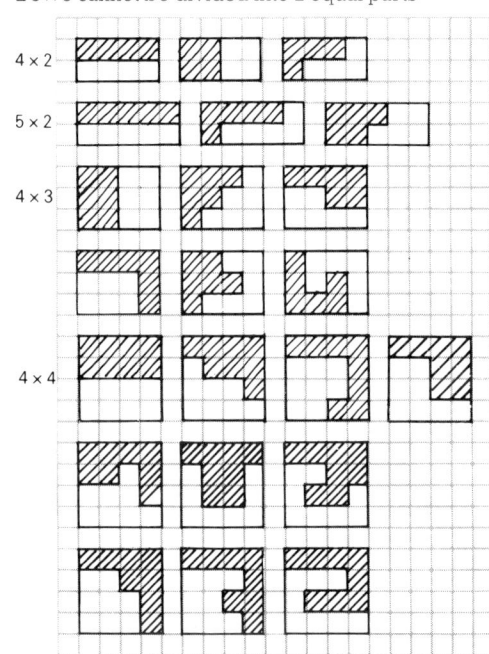

4 × 2
5 × 2
4 × 3
4 × 4

3

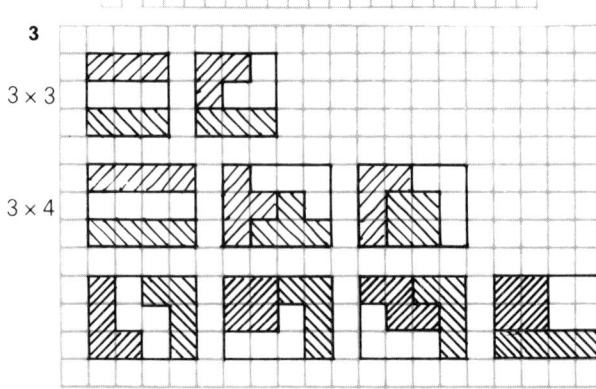

3 × 3
3 × 4

Page 19   *A magic square*

1	8	6
10	5	0
4	2	9

Total 15   Row, column and diagonal totals are all 3a

Page 19   *Model-car racing tracks*

1 a 12 straight 8 curved
3 Outer edge 334·25 cm, inner edge 271·4 cm

Page 20   *Multiplication table squares*

1 a $8 + 15 = 10 + 12 + 1$ **b** $a + d = b + c + 1$
2 a Products are equal: $ad = bc$ **b** $8 \times 15 = 2^3 \times 3 \times 5$,
$10 \times 12 = 2 \times 5 \times 2^2 \times 3 = 2^3 \times 3 \times 5$
3 a The diagonal from top left to bottom right   **b** Squares of numbers 1 to 9

Page 21   *Dinkie's bone*

1

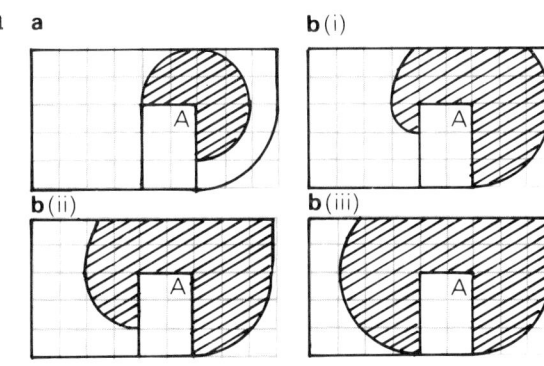

c 7 m

2

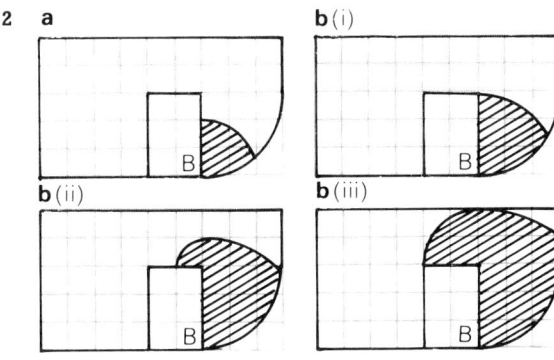

c 10 m

3 A point on the shorter side of the shed, 1·8 m from A

Page 22   *How many routes?*

1 a A → D → C   **b** A → D → E → C, A → E → D → C,
A → E → B → C
c (i) A → B → E → D → C, A → D → E → B → C
(ii) A → B → E → A → D → C, A → D → E → A → B → C,
A → E → B → A → D → C, A → E → D → A → B → C

2 a A → E → C, A → F → C   **b** A → E → F → C,
A → E → D → C, A → B → D → C, A → B → E → C,
A → F → E → C
c (i) A → E → B → D → C, A → B → E → F → C,
A → B → D → E → C, A → B → E → D → C,
A → F → E → D → C (ii) A → E → B → D → E → C,
A → B → D → E → F → C, A → F → E → B → D → C,
A → B → E → A → F → C, A → E → D → B → E → C,
A → E → B → A → F → C
3 a A → E → C   **b** A → B → E → C, A → B → D → C,
A → E → F → C, A → G → E → C, A → G → F → C,
A → E → D → C
c (i) A → B → E → F → C, A → B → E → D → C,
A → E → G → F → C, A → G → E → D → C,
A → B → D → E → C, A → G → E → F → C,
A → G → F → E → C
A → E → B → D → C (ii) A → B → E → G → F → C,
A → B → D → E → F → C, A → E → B → D → E → C,
A → G → F → E → D → C, A → E → G → F → E → C,
A → G → E → B → D → C, A → E → F → G → E → C

Page 22   *Building a brick wall*

1 45, 14. Order minimum of 630
2 b $l = 2w + t$ **c** (i) 250 mm (ii) 132·5 mm   **d** yes,
$l + t = 2w + 2t$

Page 23   *Tossing a coin*

3 coins **a** HHH, HHT, HHT, HHT, HTT, HTT, HTT, TTT
b 1, 3, 3, 1   **c** The $(n + 1)$th row gives the numbers for n coins   **d** 1, 4, 6, 4, 1; 1, 5, 10, 10, 5, 1; 1, 6, 15, 20, 15, 6, 1
e (i) $\frac{1}{4}$ (ii) $\frac{1}{8}$ (iii) $\frac{1}{16}, \frac{1}{32}, \frac{1}{64} \cdots \frac{1}{2^n}$

Page 24   *Garages and Greenhouses to order*

1 b Sides 10 m², half roof 12·5 m², doors 8 m², back 11 m² front above doors 3 m²   **c** £702

2 a

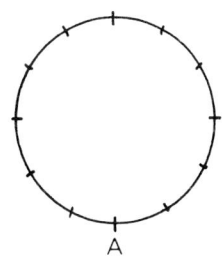

b Strips: 6 of 2 m, 12 of 1 m, 6 of 1·3 m
Glass: 6 of 2 m², 6 triangles of 0·6 m²
c 15·6 m²

Page 24   *The Big Wheel*

1 b

c

Angle (°)	0 360	30 330	60 300	90 270	120 240	150 210	180
Distance (m)	0	3·1	6	8·5	10·4	11·6	12

Page 25   *Sporting competitions*

1 a (i) 2   (ii) 6   (iii) 12   (iv) 20   (v) 90   **b** Yes 420 games
2 a (i) 7   (ii) 15   (iii) 31   (iv) $n-1$ **b** Preliminary rounds must be played or byes given into the next round

Page 26   *The Dambusters*

1 $h = 30$ ft   **2 a** 64·3 ft   **b** 73·3°   **3** 20 ft or 40 ft

Page 27   *Barn buildings*

1

	Number of sides	Number of triangles	Sum of angles
Quadrilateral	4	2	$2 \times 180°$
Pentagon	5	3	$3 \times 180°$
Hexagon	6	4	$4 \times 180°$
n-gon	n	$n-2$	$(n-2) \times 180°$

2 b 60   **3** $8x = 540$, $x = 67·5$ **4** $10x = 720$, $x = 72$

5

Number of sections	3	4	5	6	7
x	60	67·5	72	75	77·1

7 a 85   **b** 87

Page 28   *A concrete jungle*

1 a 25 m²   **b** 5 m   **c** 2·5 m
2 (i) 50 m², 7·1 m, 1·5 m   (ii) 33 m², 5·8 m, 2·1 m   (iii) 20 m², 4·5 m, 2·8 m

Page 28   *Mathematics results*

2

Grade	A	B	C	D	E	F	G	U
a % Before last	7·5	7·9	12·5	19·6	21·3	10·4	6·3	4·6
b % last	8·4	7·9	14·9	20·8	17·8	11·9	5·4	7·9

3 (i) E, D   (ii) E, D

4 a

Grade	A	B	C	D	E	F	G	U	No Exam
Number of pupils	19	16	19	37	37	25	15	7	2
%	10·7	9·0	10·7	20·9	20·9	14·1	8·5	4·0	1·1

c Good improvements in Grade A when considered as percentages, also in Grade B but a reduction in Grade C. Grades F and G remain roughly the same as numbers of pupils but increase as percentages

Page 31   *Resistor colour codes*

1 a 20   **b** 340   **c** 40 k   **d** 89 m   **e** 222   **f** 32·4 m   **g** 6·3   **h** 5·92, all in ohms
2 a Red, blue, black   **b** Green, blue, brown
c Orange, orange, red   **d** Violet, white, orange
e Violet, grey, blue   **f** Orange, yellow, gold
g Green, black, silver   **h** Blue, orange, silver, gold

Page 33   *Grid line lengths*

1 (ii) $\sqrt{(1^2 + 1^2)} = \sqrt{2}$
2 (ii) $\sqrt{(2^2 + 1^2)} = \sqrt{5}$ (iii) $\sqrt{(2^2 + 2^2)} = \sqrt{8}$

3

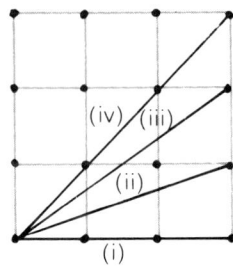

The new lengths are—
(i) 3   (ii) $\sqrt{10}$ (iii) $\sqrt{13}$ (iv) $\sqrt{18}$

4 a

Grid size	New lengths	Total number of lengths
1 by 1	1, $\sqrt{2}$	2
2 by 2	2, $\sqrt{5}$, $\sqrt{8}$	$2+3 = 5$
3 by 3	3, $\sqrt{10}$, $\sqrt{13}$, $\sqrt{18}$	$5+4 = 9$
4 by 4	4, $\sqrt{17}$, $\sqrt{20}$, 5, $\sqrt{32}$	$9+5 = 14$
5 by 5	$\sqrt{26}$, $\sqrt{29}$, $\sqrt{34}$, $\sqrt{41}$, $\sqrt{50}$	$14+5 = 19$
6 by 6	6, $\sqrt{37}$, $\sqrt{40}$, $\sqrt{45}$, $\sqrt{52}$, $\sqrt{61}$, $\sqrt{72}$	$19+7 = 26$
7 by 7	7, $\sqrt{50}$, $\sqrt{53}$, $\sqrt{58}$, $\sqrt{65}$, $\sqrt{74}$, $\sqrt{85}$, $\sqrt{98}$	$26+8 = 34$

5 $\sqrt{1}$ (1), $\sqrt{2}$, $\sqrt{4}$ (2), $\sqrt{5}$, $\sqrt{8}$, $\sqrt{9}$ (3), $\sqrt{10}$, $\sqrt{13}$, $\sqrt{16}$ (4), $\sqrt{17}$, $\sqrt{18}$, $\sqrt{20}$, $\sqrt{25}$ (5), $\sqrt{26}$, $\sqrt{29}$, $\sqrt{32}$, $\sqrt{34}$, $\sqrt{36}$ (6), $\sqrt{37}$, $\sqrt{40}$, $\sqrt{41}$, $\sqrt{45}$, $\sqrt{49}$ (7), $\sqrt{50}$

Page 33   *Combining cubes*

1 b Yes   **2** Yes   **3 a** 27   **b** Yes, 3 from A or B + 6 × 4

Page 35 *When will we meet again?*

1 b

Time		1.00	1.01	1.02	1.03	1.04	1.05	1.06
Degrees turned from top	Minute hand	0	6	12	18	24	30	36
	Hour hand	30	30·5	31	31·5	32	32·5	33

c

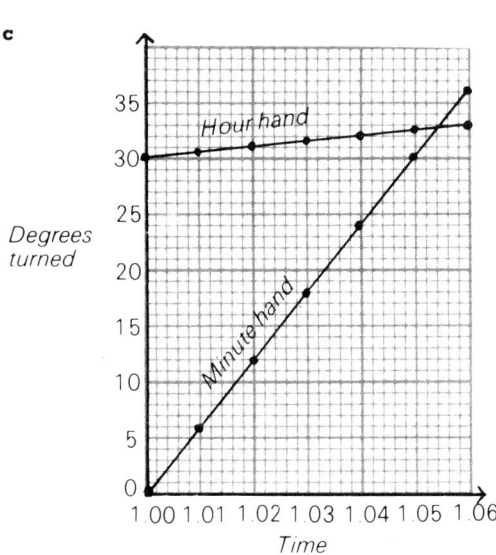

d Between 1.05 and 1.06

2 a

Time		1.05	1.06
Degrees turned	Minute hand	30°	36°
	Hour hand	32·5°	33°

b

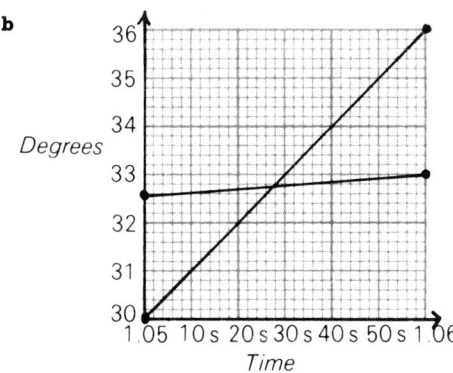

c 1.05 and 27 seconds.

Page 36 *Car brakes*

1 a Pass **b** Fail: hand brake, front wheel balance
c Fail: foot brake **d** Fail: hand brake
e Fail: foot brake, front wheel balance
f Fail: foot brake, hand brake, front wheel balance

Page 37 *Atoms and molecules*

3 Consult lattice structure in textbooks on Chemistry and books on minerals and rocks—see local library.

Page 38 *Splitting circles*

2b $A + C = C + A = 3\pi$; $B + B = 3\pi$ **c** $\frac{1}{18}, \frac{1}{6}, \frac{5}{18}$

3a $A = \frac{1}{2}\pi, B = \frac{3}{2}\pi, C = \frac{5}{2}\pi, D = \frac{7}{2}\pi$

b $A + D = \frac{1}{2}\pi + \frac{7}{2}\pi = 4\pi$; $B + C = \frac{3}{2}\pi + \frac{5}{2}\pi = 4\pi$; $\frac{1}{32}, \frac{3}{32}, \frac{5}{32}, \frac{7}{32}$

4 $E = \frac{9}{2}\pi$; $\frac{9}{50}$ **5** $\frac{2n-1}{2n^2}$

Page 39 *Number sequences*

1 $2n - 1$; $3n + 1$; $5n - 6$; $n + 9$
2 a 200 **b** 197 **c** -184 **d** -399
3
Number of squares	1	2	3	4 …	n
Number of matches	4	7	10	13 …	$3n + 1$
Perimeter	4	6	8	10 …	$2n + 2$

4 Sequence 1: $t_n = 2n^2 + 3n - 2$
Sequence 2: $t_n = 3n^2 + 4n - 4$
Sequence 3: $t_n = 6n^2 - 4n$
Sequence 4: $t_n = 2n^2 + 14n$
5 a $t_n = n^2 + n$; 10 100 **b** $t_n = n^2 + 2n$; 10 200
c $t_n = \frac{3}{2}n^2 - \frac{5}{2}n + 2$; 14 752 **d** $t_n = n^2 + 7n - 6$; 10 694
6
Figure number	1	2	3	4 …	n
Number of small triangles	1	4	9	16 …	n^2
Number of matches	3	9	18	30 …	$\frac{3}{2}n(n+1)$
Extra number of matches	3	6	9	12 …	$3n$
No. of triangles of all sizes	1	5	13	25 …	$2n^2 - 2n + 1$

8 a $t_n = 2^{n-1}$ **b** $t_n = 2 \times 3^{n-1}$ **c** $t_n = (-1)^{n-1}$ or $(-1)^{n+1}$

Page 41 *A 'Head of year' Election*

4 Oliver 47, Belinda 133

Page 43 *Launch rockets* (answers given to 3 significant figures)

2 Saturn 1B
1st stage: Volume $= 27\,700\,\text{ft}^3$;
curved surface area $= 5280\,\text{ft}^2$
2nd stage: Volume $= 20\,400\,\text{ft}^3$;
curved surface area $= 3890\,\text{ft}^2$
 Saturn 5
1st stage: Volume $= 118\,000\,\text{ft}^3$;
curved surface area $= 14\,300\,\text{ft}^2$
2nd stage: Volume $= 69\,300\,\text{ft}^3$;
curved surface area $= 8400\,\text{ft}^2$
3rd stage: Volume $= 20\,400\,\text{ft}^3$;
curved surface area $= 3890\,\text{ft}^2$

Page 44   Cubic Construction Co.

1 a 5 **b** 16 **c** 11   **2 a** 33 **b** 17

3 Kit

Kit	4	5	6	7
No. of pieces	56	85	120	161

Kit	3A	4A	5A	6A
No. of pieces	23	29	35	41

4 $6u + 5$

Page 44   The solar system

1 $T^2 = kD^3$. $1 = k \times 93^3 \Rightarrow k = \dfrac{1}{93^3}$ so $T^2 = \left(\dfrac{D}{93}\right)^3$

2 $T^2 = \left(\dfrac{36}{93}\right)^3 = (0{\cdot}387)^3 = 0{\cdot}058 \Rightarrow T = 0{\cdot}24$

Period $= 0{\cdot}24$ years $= 365 \times 0{\cdot}24$ days $= 88$ days, nearly.

3 and **4 a**

Planet	Period	Velocity (mph)	Velocity (miles/s)
Mercury	88 days	107 000	29·7
Venus	223 days	79 000	21·9
Mars	1·89 years	54 000	15·0
Jupiter	11·9 years	29 000	8·1
Saturn	29·5 years	22 000	6·0
Uranus	83·9 years	15 000	4·2
Neptune	164·5 years	12 000	3·4
Pluto	250·9 years	11 000	2·9

4 b A planet nearer to the sun moves faster than one further away.

c $V \propto \dfrac{1}{\sqrt{D}}$

d No. A planet moves faster when closer to the sun than it does when it is further away from the sun.

Page 45   Athletics World Records

1 Men: 100 m
2 b The graph is not a straight line because the longer distances are run at a slower average speed.
c (i) 2 min 10 s (ii) 4 min 40 s
d Estimate times (i) 2 min 26 s (ii) 5 min 17 s

3 a

Event		100 m	200 m	400 m	800 m	1500 m	5000 m (men) 3000 m (women)	10 000 m
Speed (men)	m/s	10·07	10·14	9·12	7·86	7·16	6·42	6·14
	km/h	36·25	36·50	32·83	28·30	25·78	23·11	22·12
Speed (women)	m/s	9·29	9·21	8·40	7·06	6·45	5·97	5·51
	km/h	33·44	33·16	30·24	25·42	23·22	21·48	19·84

b Women's times closer to the men's at shorter distances.

4 High jump: difference is 0·34 m, which is 14% (based on men's performance).
Long jump: difference is 1·45 m, which is 16% (based on men's performance).

Page 46   The treasure hunt

1

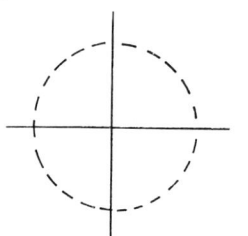

2

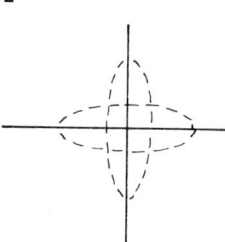

3

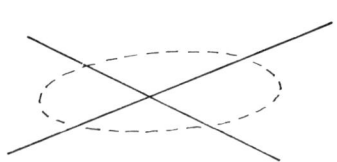

Page 47   Fractions

1 a 1·5, 1·4, 1·417, 1·414 (correct to 4 significant figures)
b 1·414213562 (calculator)

3 $\dfrac{1}{1 + \dfrac{1}{1 + \frac{1}{4}}} = \dfrac{1}{1 + \frac{4}{5}} = \dfrac{1}{\frac{9}{5}} = \dfrac{5}{9}$

4 a $\dfrac{4}{7} = \dfrac{1}{1 + \dfrac{1}{1 + \frac{1}{3}}}$ **b** $\dfrac{11}{21} = \dfrac{1}{1 + \dfrac{1}{1 + \frac{1}{10}}}$ **c** $\dfrac{13}{25} = \dfrac{1}{1 + \dfrac{1}{1 + \frac{1}{12}}}$

5 In each case, the denominator $= 2 \times$ numerator $- 1$ and the last fraction has denominator $(2n-1) - n$, so the pattern is

$\dfrac{n}{2n-1} = \dfrac{1}{1 + \dfrac{1}{1 + \dfrac{1}{n-1}}}$, n a natural number.

Page 48   Regular hexagons

1 1   12   12   **2** 4   66   156
   2   30   42   **5** 84   240
   3   48   90
3 a $12 + (n-1) \times 18 = 6(3n-1)$ **b** $3n(3n+1)$ **4** 21

Page 48   *ISBN Book Codes*

2 The check digit is the smallest number which when added to the sum of the products will make this sum exactly divisible by 11.
3 The 5 and the 9 have been interchanged   **4** 2

Page 49   *Measure for measure*

1 All thicknesses from 1 to 15 thou
2 All lengths from 1 to 8 blinks
3 Lengths of 1, 3, 9, 27, 81 blinks, by addition and subtraction, will measure every length from 1 to 121 blinks

Page 50   *Maximising volumes*

1 $8x + 4y$ metres   **2** $8x + 4y = 60$; $y = 15 - 2x$
3 a $V = x^2 y$ **b** $V = x^2(15 - 2x)$
4

x m	0	1	2	3	4	5	6	7	8
V m³	0	13	44	81	112	125	108	49	−64

6 $x = 5$ gives maximum value of V
7 $y = 20 - 2x$; $V = \frac{1}{4}\sqrt{3}x^2 y = \frac{1}{2}\sqrt{3}x^2(10 - x)$;
$x = y = 6\frac{2}{3}$ gives maximum value of V

Page 51   *Tiling a roof*

1 Next three entries are $\frac{9}{3}, \frac{11}{3}, \frac{13}{3}$; $L = \frac{1}{3}(2n + 1)$; 15 ft
2 $n = \frac{1}{2}(3L - 1)$;   **a** 22   **b** 37   **c** 60
3 a $L = \frac{1}{3}(n + 2)$ **b** $L = \frac{1}{2}(n + 1)$ **c** $L = \frac{1}{4}(n + 3)$

$$L = n\left(1 - \frac{x}{y}\right) + \frac{x}{y}$$

Page 51   *Bella's problem*

1 a 75·4 cm²   **b** 62·4 cm²   **c** 13·0 cm²

2 $A_1 = \frac{1}{6}\pi r^2$, $A_2 = \frac{1}{4}\sqrt{3}r^2$, $A_3 = \frac{1}{6}\pi r^2 - \dfrac{\sqrt{3}}{4}r^2$

Grazing area $= 2(\frac{1}{6}\pi r^2 + \frac{1}{6}\pi r^2 - \frac{1}{4}\sqrt{3}r^2)$
$\qquad\qquad = \frac{1}{6}r^2(4\pi - 3\sqrt{3})$

Percentage of the field for grazing

$= \dfrac{\frac{1}{6}r^2(4\pi - 3\sqrt{3})}{\pi r^2} \times 100$

$= \left(\dfrac{2}{3} - \dfrac{\sqrt{3}}{2\pi}\right) \times 100$

$\doteqdot 39\%$

Page 52   *A Bypass*

1 a (i) After 07 00, there was a large increase in traffic into and through Queuetown.
(ii) Much traffic left Queuetown.

b

Time	Net flow in	Time	Net flow in
6–7	+16	14–15	−61
7–8	+615	15–16	−329
8–9	+1059	16–17	−587
9–10	+51	17–18	−811
10–11	+.14	18–19	−303
11–12	+79	19–20	−252
12–13	−11	20–21	−162
13–14	−32		

c

Time	East at A	West at A
7	45	15
8	607	258
9	1550	518
10	2022	781
11	2437	1020
12	2826	1203
13	3088	1453
14	3372	1771
15	3734	2167
16	4118	2629
17	4442	3257
18	4865	4200
19	5083	4724
20	5223	5040
21	5301	5234

2a

Time	(i)	(ii)
6–7	163	152
7–8	1215	1275
8–9	2090	2014
9–10	1450	1503
10–11	1119	1194
11–12	968	1016
12–13	900	846
13–14	1033	1053
14–15	1356	1369
15–16	1330	1304
16–17	1533	1517
17–18	1968	1678
18–19	879	790
19–20	404	423
20–21	339	320

b (i) 4679   (ii) 4678
c (i) More goes East than West.
(ii) There is an even flow East and West.

Page 54   *A camping catalogue*

1 a, b

Type of tent	Volume (m³)	Area of material (m²)	Area of groundsheet (m²)
Wigwam	0·96	4·40	1·54
Box	1·13	5·25	1·5
Cyclist	0·42	3·18	1·4
Pyramid	1·62	6·3	3·24
Bell	1·07	4·02	2·01
Semicircle	1·19	5·09	2·52
Ridge	1·66	6·98	2·21

2 Pyramid and bell tents

3a

Type of tent	Cost of material (£)
Wigwam	26·84
Box	30
Cyclist	21·12
Pyramid	44·64
Bell	28·14
Semicircle	35·48
Ridge	41·18

b Ridge, bell and box

Page 55   *Repayment mortgages*

1 a 12% **b** 27% **c** £1440 ÷ 12 = £120

2

Amount owing		£9436·00
Gross interest	£1132·32	
Tax relief	305·73	
Net interest	826·59	826·59
Total owing		10 262·59
Less repayment		1440·00
Amount owing	30 Sep 1989	£8822·59

3

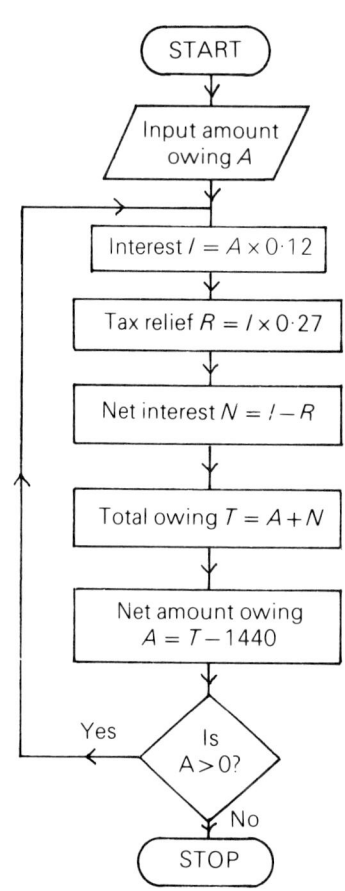

START

Input amount owing A

Interest $I = A \times 0·12$

Tax relief $R = I \times 0·27$

Net interest $N = I - R$

Total owing $T = A + N$

Net amount owing $A = T - 1440$

Is $A > 0$?

Yes

No

STOP

4 At present rates, loan is paid off during 2nd month of 12th year.
a (i) Loan is paid off during 10th month of 12th year.
(ii) Loan is paid off during 7th month of the 11th year.
b Loan is paid off during the 9th year.

Page 56   *The wheel of fortune*

1

Flash angle	No. of flashes	No. of times
10°	36	1
20°	18	1
30°	12	1
40°	9	1
50°	36	5
60°	6	1
70°	36	7
80°	9	2
90°	4	1
100°	18	5

2 a 9 **b** 6

Page 56   *Throwing light on cameras*

1 a (i) 8·04 cm² (ii) 4·02 cm² **b** 1·13 cm

2

Setting	Area	Radius
1·0	16·08	2·26
1·4	8·04	1·60
2·0	4·02	1·13
2·8	2·01	0·80
4·0	1·005	0·57
5·6	0·503	0·41
8·0	0·252	0·28
11	0·126	0·20
16	0·063	0·14
22	0·032	0·10
32	0·016	0·07
45	0·008	0·05
64	0·004	0·04

4 $sr = 2·26$ (approximately)
5 a 90·5 and 128
b Next f-number = $\sqrt{2}s$.
(The f-numbers form a geometric sequence whose common ratio is $\sqrt{2}$. For convenience, some of these are rounded off to the nearest whole number or to one decimal place.)

Page 58   *Clothes poles*

1

Number of poles	1	2	3	4	5	6 ... n
Maximum number	0	1	3	6	10	15 ... $\frac{1}{2}n(n-1)$
Minimum number	0	1	2	3	4	5 ... $(n-1)$

3 Possible with 5 but not with 6. Possible with an odd number of poles. Not possible with an even number of poles

Page 58   *Wind chill*

1 a 1178, bitterly cold **b** 455, cool **c** 1359·7, flesh almost freezes. (Given formula is correct for m/s.)

2

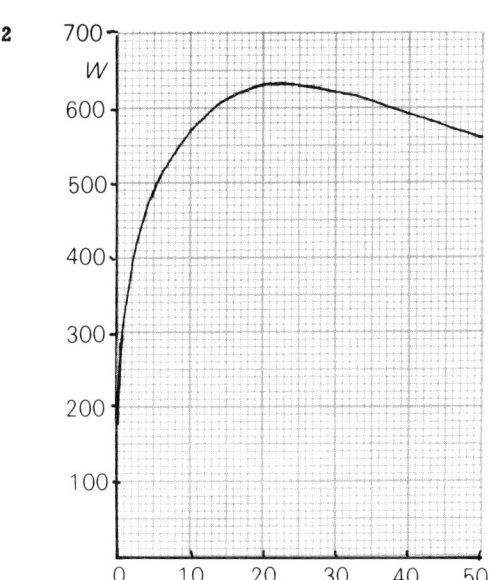

3

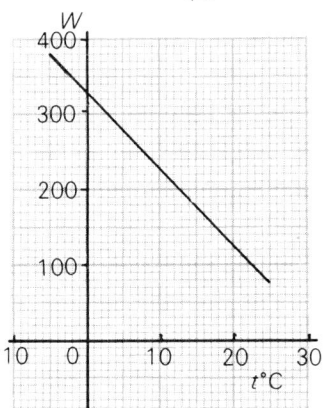

Page 59   *Car parking*

1

Angle of parking (°)	0	35	50	70	90
Number of cars		17	25	32	40	43

2 Estimates for— 45° parking: 30   60° parking: 36

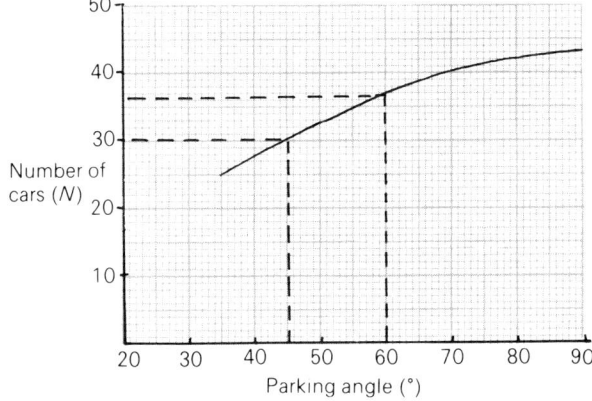

3 a 2·2 m, 4·44 m, 4·94 m, 5·07 m, 4·6 m.
(For an $\alpha°$ parking, the projection distance =
$4·6 \sin\alpha° + 2·2 \cos\alpha°$)
b 90° parking, provided that there is enough space outside
the cars.

Page 60   *Circles round triangles round circles round ...*

1 a (i) 2 (ii) 4 (iii) 8 **b** Radius of nth circle = 2^{n-1}
2 a $2\sqrt{3}, 4\sqrt{3}, 8\sqrt{3}$ **b** Length of nth side = $2^n\sqrt{3}$ units
3 a Area of nth circle = $\pi \times 2^{2n-2}$
b Area of nth triangle = $3\sqrt{3} \times 2^{n-2}$

Page 62   *Areas and volumes*

1 a $V = x^2y$ **b** $x:y = 2:1$ **2 a** $V = \pi x^2 y$ **b** $x:y = 1:1$

3 a $V = \dfrac{\sqrt{3}}{4}x^2y$ **b** $x:y = 2\sqrt{3}:1$

4 a $V = \frac{1}{3}x^2\sqrt{(y^2-\frac{1}{2}x^2)}$ **b** $2x^2 = 2x\sqrt{(y^2-\frac{1}{4}x^2)} \Rightarrow x:y = 2:\sqrt{5}$

Page 63   *Communications around the world*

1

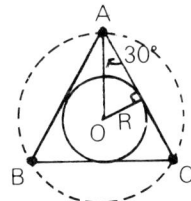

$\sin 30° = \dfrac{R}{\text{AO}} \Rightarrow \text{AO} = \dfrac{R}{\sin 30°} = 2R.$
So height above the earth's surface = $2R - R = R$

2

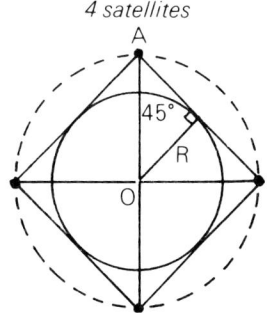

4 satellites

$\text{AO} = \dfrac{R}{\sin 45°} = \sqrt{2}R.$
So height above the earth's surface = $\sqrt{2}R - R$
$\doteqdot 0·414R$

5 satellites

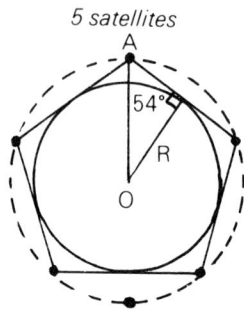

$$AO = \frac{R}{\sin 54°} \doteqdot 1{\cdot}236R.$$

So height above the earth's surface $\doteqdot 0{\cdot}236R$

6 satellites

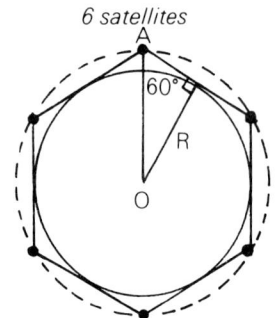

$$AO = \frac{R}{\sin 60°} = \frac{2}{\sqrt{3}}R \doteqdot 1{\cdot}155R.$$

So height above the earth's surface $\doteqdot 0{\cdot}155R$

3 Angle at the centre for n satellites $= \dfrac{360°}{n}$

4 $C = kh$. Cheaper to have a large number of satellites

Page 63   *Rockets and cones*

1 a $\frac{10}{3}\pi$ cm   **b** $1\frac{2}{3}$ cm $\doteqdot 1{\cdot}67$ cm   **c** $9{\cdot}86$ cm

2

Sector angle ($x°$)	60°	120°	180°	240°	300°
Height of cone (h cm)	9·9	9·4	8·7	7·5	5·5

3

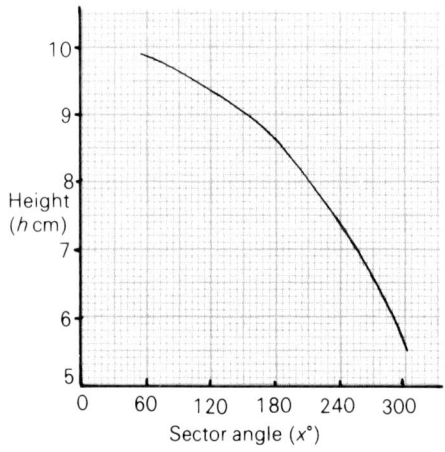

4 Circumference of base $= \dfrac{\pi x}{18}$.

Radius of base r is given by $2\pi r = \dfrac{\pi x}{18}$, so

$$r = \frac{x}{36}.$$

Using Pythagoras' Theorem,

$$h^2 = 10^2 - \left(\frac{x}{36}\right)^2 = 100 - \left(\frac{x}{36}\right)^2$$

Page 64   *Triblockbusters*

Note that x $\geqslant$ 0.   **1** 5, 1, 4   **2** 2, 3, 1   **3** 1, 2, 3
4 1, 2, 3 and 2, 2, 4   **5** 2, 3, 5 and 1, 6, 7   **6** 2, 6, 8
7 12, 24, 36 and 3, 9, 12   **8** 4, 4, 8   **9** 24, 84, 108 and 12, 4, 16

Page 65   *Domino dots*

1

Highest double	0	1	2	3	4	5	6
No. of dominoes in set	1	3	6	10	15	21	28

2 (i) 66   (ii) $\frac{1}{2}(n+1)(n+2)$

3

Highest double	0	1	2	3	4	5	6
Extra no. of dots to etch	0	3	9	18	30	45	63
Total no. of dots to etch	0	3	12	30	60	105	168

Page 66   *Chess ladders*

a 2 players, 1   **b** 3 players, 3   **c** 4 players, 6   **d** 5 players, 10
e.g. for 5 players, the bottom player needs to win 4, the
next needs to win 3 and so on giving $(4+3+2+1) = 10$.
Formula for n players $= 1+2+3+ \ldots +(n-1) = \frac{1}{2}n(n-1)$

Page 66   *A round table*

2 Start by drawing a circle, radius 5 cm, with four
diameters set at 45°. Now construct the three horizontal
and vertical four-sided strips. To do this, mark two points
such as A, B near the ends of a diameter. With centres A
and B describe arcs of radius 0·6 cm. Draw lines CD and
EF touching these arcs, terminated by the circumference
of the circle. Similarly, construct in opposite pairs, the four
five-sided strips. Erase the guide-lines and so complete
the outline required.

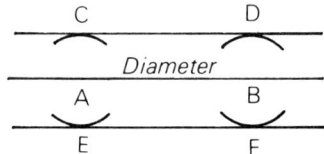

Page 66   *Football league competition*

1 a

Number of teams	2	3	4	5	6	7	8
Maximum penalty points	2	4	8	12	18	24	32

b (i) 200   (ii) 220   **c** (i) $n^2/2$ (ii) $(n-1)(n+1)/2$

Page 67   *Rolling polygons*

Equilateral triangle: Arc 1 $= \frac{1}{3} \times 2\pi \times 1 = \frac{2}{3}\pi$ units
                Arc 2 $= \frac{2}{3}\pi$ units
                Total length of path $= \frac{2}{3}\pi + \frac{2}{3}\pi$
                                $= \frac{4}{3}\pi$ units.

Square: $\text{Arc } 1 + \text{arc } 2 + \text{arc } 3 = \frac{1}{4} \cdot 2\pi + \frac{1}{4} \cdot 2\pi\sqrt{2} + \frac{1}{4} \cdot 2\pi$

$$= \frac{\pi}{2} + \frac{\sqrt{2}\pi}{2} + \frac{\pi}{2}$$

$$= \pi + \frac{\sqrt{2}}{2}\pi$$

$$= \frac{\pi}{2}(2 + \sqrt{2}) \text{ units.}$$

Regular hexagon: $AD = 2AO = 2AB = 2 \text{ units}$
$$AC = AD \cos CAO = 2 \cos 30°$$

$$= 2 \times \frac{\sqrt{3}}{2} = \sqrt{3} \text{ units}$$

$\text{Arc } 1 = \text{arc } 5 = \dfrac{\pi}{3} \text{ units}$

$\text{Arc } 2 = \text{arc } 4 = \dfrac{\sqrt{3}}{3}\pi \text{ units}$

$\text{Arc } 3 = \dfrac{2\pi}{3} \text{ units}$

Total length $= \frac{2}{3}(2 + \sqrt{3})\pi$ units.

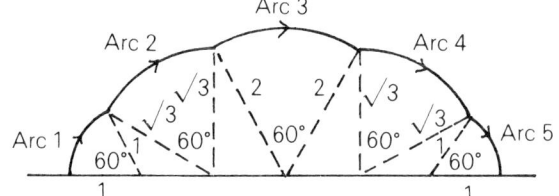

Brainstormers

Page 69

1 In pence: 13, 18, 26, 31, 36, 39, 44, 49, 52, 54, 57, 62, 65, 67, 70, 72, 75, 78, 80, 83, 85, 88, 90, 91, 93, 96, 98
2 Saturn 6 g, Crescent 4 g, Star 5 g
3 a 8 cubes with three red faces
b 8 cubes with three red faces, 12 cubes with two red faces,
6 cubes with one red face and 1 cube with no red face.
4 a Add up in 10's. Total 100
b $\frac{1}{2}(1 + 100) \times 100 = 5050$ **c** 16 (Area of square)

Page 70

5 a 2 pts; $2 + 2$ into 7 giving 4 pts; $2 + 2 + 2$ into 7 giving 6 pts; $(2 + 2 + 2 \text{ into } 7) + 2$ giving 8 pts; $7 + 2$ giving 9 pts; 7 pts; $7 - 2$ giving 5 pts; $7 - 2 - 2$ giving 3 pts; $7 - 2 - 2 - 2$ giving 1 pt
b 1, 2, 3, 4, 5, ..., 15, 16 pts
c 3 pt and 7 pt jugs
6 Distances, to nearest mm, from top midpoint, are 5 ($3 \tan 10°$), 11, 17, 25, 36, 53 and 82; also on LHS and RHS, 26 mm from base ($15 \tan 10°$)

Page 71

7 a $t_1 = \frac{1}{2}, t_2 = \frac{1}{3}, t_3 = \frac{1}{4}, \ldots; t_n = \dfrac{1}{n+1}$

b $t_1 = 1 - \frac{1}{2}, t_2 = 1 - \frac{1}{3}, t_3 = 1 - \frac{1}{4}, \ldots; t_n = 1 - \dfrac{1}{n+1}$

c $t_1 = \dfrac{2}{2+1}, t_2 = \dfrac{2}{2+2}, t_3 = \dfrac{2}{2+3}, \ldots; t_n = \dfrac{2}{2+n}$

d $t_1 = \dfrac{1}{2+1}, t_2 = \dfrac{2}{2+2}, t_3 = \dfrac{3}{2+3}, \ldots; t_n = \dfrac{n}{2+n}$

8

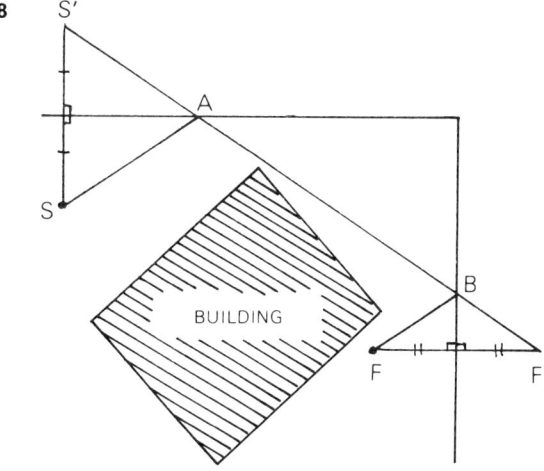

9 Suppose that $a = n-1$, $b = n$, $c = n+1$ and $d = n+2$, where n is a natural number.
(i) $bc - ad = n(n+1) - (n-1)(n+2) = n^2 + n - (n^2 + n - 2) = 2$
(ii) $bd - ac = n(n+2) - (n-1)(n+1) = 2n + 1$, which is odd
(iii) $a + b + c + d = n - 1 + n + n + 1 + n + 2 = 4n + 2$
$$= 2 \times (2n + 1)$$
$$= 2 \times \text{odd number}$$
(iv) $a^2 + d^2 = (n-1)^2 + (n+2)^2 = 2n^2 + 2n + 5$
$b^2 + c^2 + 4 = n^2 + (n+1)^2 + 4 = 2n^2 + 2n + 5$

Page 72

10 a (i)

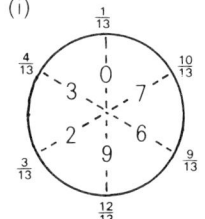

(ii)

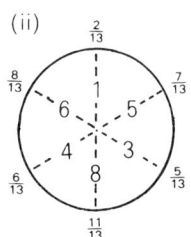

b (i)

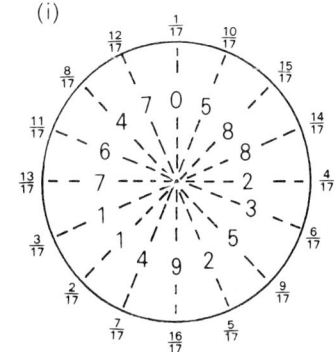

(ii)

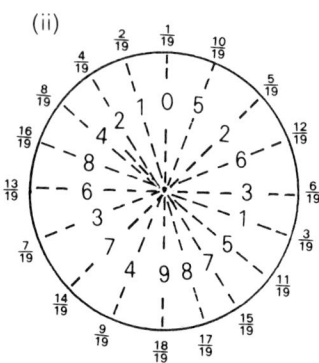

16 a The tanks would have to contain 8, −1 and 4 gallons, which is not possible.

b (i) 2, then the process continues indefinitely (ii) 3 (iii) 4

c Tanks contain a, b, c gallons.

Then $2a$, $2b$, $c-a-b$ gallons.

So $c-a-b \geqslant 0$, or $c \geqslant a+b$.

d 1, 1, 22; 1, 4, 19; 1, 7, 16; 1, 10, 13; 4, 7, 13

11 a (i) 2, 4, 8, 16, 32, 64, 128, 256, . . .

(ii) Yes. 2, 4, 8, 6, 2, 4, 8, 6, 2, 4, 8, 6, . . .

(iii) 6

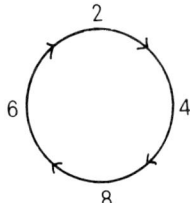

b (i) 3, 9, 27, 81, 243, 729, 2187, 6561, . . .

(ii) Yes. 3, 9, 7, 1, 3, 9, 7, 1, . . .

(iii) 1

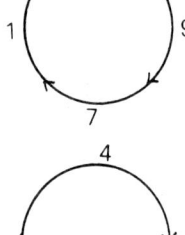

(i) 4, 16, 64, 246, 1024, 4096, . . .

(ii) Yes. 4, 6, 4, 6, 4, 6, . . .

(iii) 6

(i) 5, 25, 125, 625, 3125, . . .

(ii) Yes. Last digit is always a 5.

(iii) 5

Page 73

12 a

m	l^2+b^2	h^2
1	169	169
2	841	841
3	2809	2809

b $l^2+b^2 = (64m^2+64m+16)+(16m^4+32m^3-8m^2-24m+9)$

$\qquad = 16m^4+32m^3+56m^2+40m+25$

$\quad h^2 = (4m^2+4m+5)^2$

$\qquad = 16m^4+32m^3+56m^2+40m+25$

13 No. There could be 68, 188, 308, . . . present. The formula is $N = 120n+68$, where $n = 0, 1, 2, . . .$

14 a $65 = 1^2+8^2$ or 4^2+7^2

b 9 and 10, or 12 and 1

15   37 964

　　　　 × 20

　　　 ─────

　　 759 280

　　　 ─────

Note the four pairs of common digits:
0, 0; 2, 2; 9, 9; 7, 7.